A STORMY NIGHT

"... the clearest subject may be overclouded by mere superabundance of talk ... In one case out of a hundred a point is excessively discussed because it is obscure; in the ninety-nine remaining it is obscure because excessively discussed. When a topic is thus circumstanced, the readiest mode of investigating it is to forget that any previous investigation has been attempted."

Edgar Allan Poe *(The Rationale of Verse)*

A STORMY NIGHT

with The Turn Of The Screw

by
MURIEL WEST

FRYE & SMITH, LTD., PHOENIX

For
LEON EDEL
whose kind advice, intuitive
wisdom, and concern for truth
have made this work possible.

L.C. Card Catalog Number 64-22898
Copyright © 1964
Muriel West.
All Rights Reserved.

CONTENTS

Introduction vii
Facsimile Page x
Foreword xi

I	I Was Alone!..	1
II	Of Course I Was Impressed....................	5
III	On The Alert..	13
IV	I Poured...	21
V	But I Hated..	25
VI	But Sometimes Answers........................	29
VII	When I Examined................................	37
VIII	Believing I Had Solved........................	43
IX	Starting Down The Stairs......................	53
X	I Crossed The Hall...............................	61
XI	I Was About To See.............................	67
XII	Suddenly...	71

INTRODUCTION

Aside from the novelty of its colloquial first-person narrative style, the following account of a reading of *The Turn of the Screw* is perhaps most noteworthy for its avoidance (whether by accident or design) of the seemingly endless controversy over the interpretation of Henry James's well-known "fairy-tale" or "pot-boiler," as he variously called it. The anonymous author argues with no one but himself; he questions the logic and good sense of no observations but his own. And yet his own complex of opinions (somewhat predetermined by his background and his innate attitude towards the supernatural) rather add up on the side of the "hallucinationists"—but with differences and modifications.

In a general way, *A Stormy Night* (I have taken the liberty of giving the strange narrative a name) may fairly be called an exploration based on the study of several possible literary influences—an exploration not hitherto undertaken in any thorough-going way—perhaps because it leads to a heterogeneous assemblage of opinions and suggestive ideas not easily coerced into a clean-cut conclusion. Such as they are in their suggestiveness, these ideas come closer, perhaps, to opinions expressed or implied by Edna Kenton, Harold McCarthy, Seymour Lainoff, Edmund Wilson, Oscar Cargill, J. A. Wood, Harold C. Goddard, John Lydenberg, John Silver, and Leon Edel than they do to those put forth by scores of other scholars and critics who have been challenged into print by the ambiguities of *The Turn of the Screw*. One is strongly reminded of Miss Kenton's assumption that the governess wrote an imaginative rather than a factual account of her experiences at Bly, and of Edel's suggestion that James drew on many experiences — including his travels and his reading.

The manuscript (which came into my hands by a lucky chance — included in a box of miscellaneous old books bought at auction) is contained in two old stiff-backed notebooks, such as might have been intended for the keeping of household accounts. The complicated ruling in blue and red for columns of figures has been ignored both by the original writer and by his discoverer and annotator who signs himself merely by initials — H. K. Y. The recto pages are covered with the text proper written in a rapid scrawl in faded or brown ink with seldom a scratch-out or revision; in fact, the hastiness of composition is evident in the off-set blots that disfigure the lower portions of many of the facing pages. Disfigured though they be, these verso pages are still clean enough to allow room for H. K. Y. to write (with numerous revisions in wording, and in a stiff cramped hand in black ink) his rather querulous notes — these carefully marked with guiding arrows to show where he intended their insertion in the text. Although he may have intended that these comments should ultimately be handled in footnotes, I have inserted them, in brackets, in the places indicated. Aside from the correction of a few accidental errors in spelling and the addition of an occasional comma for clarity, I have, in preparing the curious manuscript for publication, scrupulously followed the text.

For the most part, H. K. Y.'s notes require no comment. But I question his assumption that the manuscript was written sometime "subsequent to 1905 and prior to 1908." Perhaps he sets these limits on the basis of the author's detailed familiarity with the travel sketches contained in *English Hours* (first published in 1905) and the 1908 publication date of Volume XII of the *Novels and Tales*. It must be remembered that all of these sketches appeared earlier (some of them much earlier) in various magazines; and that the use of the 1898 edition of *The Turn of the Screw* (or of reprints based on it) is common practice. Insofar as H. K. Y.'s suggested limits may depend on the use of oil lamps and candles—well, one might as sensibly say that because no timepiece seems present in the old house, the manuscript was written before the invention of clocks and watches.

To Mary Jean Gross, Allen Cohn, Evelyn Berdahl, Evan Hacker, Frederick R. Rebsamen, and Jack L. Cross I wish to express my appreciation for valuable assistance of various kinds in preparing the manuscript for publication.

Southern Illinois University
Carbondale, Illinois
January, 1964   Muriel West

FOREWORD

On discovering (in the secret compartment of an antiquated brass and mahogany desk—found in the attic of an old house on W⎯⎯⎯n Square) an old manuscript containing an anonymous critical opinion of Henry James's *The Turn of the Screw*, its discoverer naturally feels himself obligated to present so curious a document to the literate public.

The anonymous author's style—it may be noted—is, if viewed from modern standards, remarkably unscholarly. Imagine *beginning* a critical review with the first-person-singular, and with such a phrase: "I was alone"! Although the manuscript bears no date, internal evidence suggests a period of our era subsequent to 1905 and prior to 1908. Such a circumstance may fairly be said, in a sense, to give the unknown author and his criticism an interest that compensates somewhat for the heedlessness of his diction (not one iota of which has been changed!) and for his inability to arrive at unimpeachable conclusions. Certain interpretative notes have been appended for clarity.

H. K. Y.

Chapter I

I WAS ALONE!

And a great relief it was on a cold and stormy night to find myself so. The others had gone, I thanked the Lord Harry, to spend Christmas in town. So, contrary to my usual custom of calling it a day about dark, I made up my mind to make a night of it. I dragged in great logs, made a roaring fire (like the third little pig anticipating the last visit from the wolf), set the gray agate picnic coffee pot on the hearth with enough of the good old Java to last me through the wee small [*hours?*] and pulled a big chair near the fire where *I* wanted it—to catch up (for once) with a number of too-easily-made promises. Among other things I had long before given my solemn word to write a critique on James's *Turn of the Screw* for my old friend and classmate, Baldy Twitchell [*research has failed to reveal either the identity of or the connection of this indecorously denominated gentleman with any known journal of the presumed day*]. I found the book under a stack of as-yet-uncorrected proof sheets of my *Attributes of Gothic* (to be published in the spring) [*exhaustive search has failed to produce any information on such a work*], placed the big lamp exactly where *I* wanted it on a table to my left, poured myself a cup of steaming coffee, and sat down to read.

But no sooner had I done so than a great stream of wind howled down the chimney—scattering ashes and sparks for six or eight feet around the hearth. At the same time the front door blew open and cold wind raced through the corridor into the room. The lamp flared high, flickered almost out, but re-

A Stormy Night

covered itself. Of course I rushed to the entrance, pushed the heavy door to — against the hideous strength of the icy blast, and threw the bolt.

"Wonderful!" I said to the cat who had taken advantage of the open door to come in. "Wonderful! I am in a Gothic novel!" Of course I was amusing myself by remembering that Henry James had tried to kid himself in the same way — arriving at some famed castle in Scotland, approaching through the long Scotch [*Scottish*] twilight (he had a way of measuring those interminable twilights with watch in hand) and being greeted by some high-born dame who poked her head from a window of the clocktower — Anyway, *he* said to *himself,* "I am in a Waverly Novel!" Not that he believed it. He went on to tell about reading *Red Gauntlet* over again a few days later and deciding he'd been wrong for years — the book was mere rubbish.

[The passage our author refers to in his inelegant way may be found in *The Notebooks of Henry James* (New York, 1947), pp. 36-37. Comparison shows the laxity of our author's scholarship: James used the *past* tense ("I *was* in a Waverly Novel" — italics the present writer's); James did *not* say Scott's novel was "mere rubbish," but the following: "I was amazed at the badness of R.: l'enfance de l'art." Also, research has not been able to determine that James ever measured the Scottish twilight "watch in hand"; he does however, refer to the practice in describing a visit *in England:* "Such a pleasure I lately enjoyed quite in its perfection, in a walk to Haddon Hall, along a meadow path by the Wye, in this interminable English twilight which I am never weary of admiring watch in hand" (*English Hours,* London, 1960, p. 51).]

Is it any wonder that, as I settled myself to read *The Turn of the Screw,* I soon became suspicious? Even before I had finished the little preamble to the tale I suspected that dear old James was putting *some*body in a Gothic novel; by the time I had toured the old house with little Flora (that "rosy sprite") and the nervous governess (not to be confused with the other one, the charming one of the preamble), had seen a ghost evoked on the old crenelated tower, and heard the governess's provocative question in the beginning of Chapter 4: "Was there a 'secret' at Bly — a mystery of Udolpho or an insane, an unmentionable relative kept in unsuspected confinement?" I was ready to put up my money that the nervous governess

with The Turn of the Screw

of the tale, guided by the "beautiful hand" of the one in the preamble, was acting by proxy for James himself—poor old James, who could never make his own experiences with ghosts quite come off.

All over England he had tried to bring them to life—not so much ghosts of real people as ghosts of characters in novels and plays. He would say he *expected* to see Gwendolen (in a George Eliot novel) walk out of a group of English girls playing tennis, but she didn't come. Or he'd think of Olivia or Malvolio or Beatrix on a certain stately flight of steps at Haddon Hall. Or he'd try to fool himself about the beer-drinking vagrants at Kenilworth (where even the echoes in the old ruin dropped their *h*'s, in keeping with the general "cockneyfication") and pretend they were Shakespearean clowns and that he (James!) would go, in just a moment, into an alehouse and ask Mrs. Quickly for a cup of sack. In Warwickshire he even tried to turn a pasture into a stage set for a comedy. But nothing ever materialized for him. Perhaps he was afraid. Going to bed in an old house that had been an abbey, taking a devilishly daring shortcut through empty rooms and long corridors, he admits he didn't know if he was afraid he'd see a ghost or hoped he would; the servants had said there was one.

[Except for a certain corruption of James's language, our author gives a fairly exact account of the situations he alludes to. See *English Hours,* pp. 127, 53, 125-126, 135.]

Or perhaps he simply lacked, to use a term of his own, "the proper credulity."

Oh, yes, I suspected, as I sat there reading that stormy night, that James was using the governess as his proxy—putting *her* in a Gothic novel, having *her* see ghosts that he himself had never been able to bring back from the dead. Certainly his wish was strong: he would have "peopled all this isle" (to borrow a phrase from Caliban) with ghosts—if he had had it in his power.

Chapter II

OF COURSE I WAS IMPRESSED

with James's skill in picking out the most characteristic, the most typical, of the stock situations and devices of Gothic: the ancient manuscript so useful in turning back time and giving a shot in the arm to latent credulity, the old house at Bly with its two towers, the remarkable synchronization between horrifying events and natural phenomena—the candles blown out at critical moments, the blasts of icy wind announcing or attending the apparitions, and the inevitable fixed stare of these creatures, to say nothing of the nervous tremors of the governess and her remarkable aspects as a heroine. What marvelous courage! What persistence! With, of course, a good admixture of exhibitionism. It all seemed to fit together like the pieces of a Chinese puzzle—if I could just find that *certain* piece.

Imagine my delight when I came across that "certain piece" in Chapter 9—a syntactically involved Jamesian sentence almost hidden from observation by its being tucked away between: 1) a horror-build-up—the governess's promising to tell what was "hideous" at Bly, to renew what she "suffered," and to push her way through to the end; and 2) gripping narrative—of her third "encounter" or "collision" with the apparition "on the spot nearest the window," where, "with a glimmer in the high glass and another on the polish of the oak stair below," she and the ghost of Peter Quint faced each other with their "common intensity." It would be easy to race right over

A Stormy Night

the tell-tale passage, hurrying on to find out what horrible thing is going to happen next. If I hadn't been on the alert I suppose I would have missed the half-hidden sentence:

> There was a roomful of old books at Bly—last-century fiction some of it, which, to the extent of a distinctly deprecated renown, but never to so much as that of a stray specimen, had reached the sequestered home and appealed to the unavowed curiosity of my youth.

So she had read no eighteenth-century novels before she came to Bly! How then was she able to speak so knowingly, five chapters earlier, of a possible "secret" at Bly, of a "mystery of Udolpho," of a relative "kept in unsuspected confinement"? Aha, I thought, the sly minx has been making up for her "small smothered life" as the youngest daughter of a poor country parson! She has been investigating that "roomful of old books"!

On that particular night she didn't go to bed at all but sat up reading by the dim light of a couple of candles. She suddenly looked straight up from her "author" and hard at the door of the room—sensing that there was something "undefinably astir" in the house. She took a candle when she went bravely (she had been reading of that staunch heroine, Fielding's Amelia, who met no ghosts to be sure, but who never gave up in her tender care of her two dear innocent children) to investigate. Her candle went out, but she perceived that the "yielding dusk of earliest morning rendered it unnecessary," and she "saw that there was someone on the stair."

> [In giving this quotation our author reveals that he was not familiar with the New York Edition wherein James, in his revision, replaced the word "saw" with the word "knew," and "someone" with "a figure." See *The Novels and Tales* (New York, 1908), XII, 222.]

Thus she lets it out that she stayed up all night. Naturally she is in fine shape for "seeing things"! I confess I had to look back through the book to prove to myself that I was right in supposing she almost never slept. In the beginning of Chapter 2, she admits "a second sleepless night"; and later on, in Chapter 10, after her "collision" on the stairs with the ghost of Peter Quint, she lets the cat out of the bag: "You may imagine the general complexion, from that moment, of my nights. I repeatedly sat up until I didn't know when."

with The Turn of the Screw

During those trying sleepless nights she steals out from her room every now and then for a round of valorous ghost-hunting (probably between chapters in her omnivorous reading), but she has no luck, except for a brief glimpse of Miss Jessel; and on the eleventh night she tries going back to bed at her "old hour." What books and how many books of eighteenth-century fiction did she devour in that more than ten-day stretch? And how much did they stimulate her already lively imagination? I could only guess. She worries about the lapse in her ability to envision horrors, perplexing Mrs. Grose by saying it would distress her much more to lose her "power" than to keep it. Although she thinks it blasphemous not to thank God that her eyes are temporarily "sealed," she does not thank him.

Even in the daytime she has to shut herself up "to think," to "ask herself" inane questions, and to "rehearse" what she might sometime say to the children in open accusation. "Repeatedly," she says (after her first "collision"), "I dipped into my room and locked the door"—for the purpose (according to her) of saying to herself that someone "curious in old houses" had taken a "liberty rather gross" in making his way in unobserved to enjoy the prospect "from the best point of view"—that is, from the crenelated tower. More fishy reasons for locking oneself up I could not imagine. It seemed to me far more likely that she intended to "dip" privately into those books that "not to so much as a stray specimen [,] had reached the sequestered home and appealed to the unavowed curiosity" of her youth. Unless—but it was really unthinkable—she, like the fantastic governess in Le Fanu's *Uncle Silas,* dipped into her room for a swig of brandy, or, following the romantic fashion of the poets of the day, experimented with English opium-eating.

In one place I thought I caught the little bookworm in the very act of extracting from some old thriller the juice for her imaginative report on the ugly particulars of Peter Quint's death—of inventing (thus inspired) what Mrs. Grose had "kept back." Or it might be she read a while, dozed and dreamed a while, and thus produced her astonishing set of

A Stormy Night

"facts." I was particularly fascinated by her contrivance, because she said, two pages earlier, that "no discomfortable legend, no perturbation of scullions, had ever, within anyone's memory, attached to the kind old place" that had "neither bad name nor ill fame."

Mrs. Grose had resisted her pressure to reveal the details of Peter Quint's "presence, his history, . . . the circumstances of his death," a resistance that made the governess say: "I was, in the immediate later hours in especial—for it may be imagined whether I slept—still haunted with the shadow of something she had not told me." But a resourceful bookworm can quite efficiently fill in such lack of "details." She obviously makes a night of it again—and a long night at that: "It seems to me indeed, in retrospect, that by the time the morrow's sun was high I had restlessly read into the facts before us almost all the meaning they were to receive from subsequent and more cruel occurrences." In what comes next her "they" seems to refer to "facts," but she might have had "books" in her mind:

> What they gave me above all was just the sinister figure of the living man—the dead one would keep awhile!—and the months he had passed at Bly, which, added up, made a formidable stretch. The limit of this evil time had arrived only when, on the dawn of a winter's morning, Peter Quint was found, by a labourer going to early work, stone dead on the road from the village: a catastrophe explained—superficially at least—by a visible wound to his head; such a wound as might have been produced and as, on the final evidence, *had* been—by a fatal slip, in the dark and after leaving the public house, on the steepish icy slope, a wrong path, altogether, at the bottom of which he lay. The icy slope, the turn mistaken at night and in liquor, accounted for much—practically, in the end and after the inquest and boundless chatter, for everything; but there had been matters in his life—strange passages and perils, secret disorders, vices more than suspected—that would have accounted for a good deal more.

How could such a sordid death, followed by an inquest and "boundless chatter," be made to square with the governess's earlier statement that "no discomfortable legend, no perturbation of scullions, had ever, to anyone's memory, attached to the kind old place"? It obviously couldn't. Following the example of Sophia Lee and Ann Radcliffe, of revealing ghosts or hidden indefinite crimes in a dream, the governess, I realized,

with The Turn of the Screw

had either dreamed the scandalous death of Peter Quint or more likely—since she says "it may be imagined whether I slept"—she drew her facts from the book or books that kept her occupied until the "morrow's sun was high." The expressions "story," "credible picture," and "state of mind" in what she goes on to say, pretty well clinch it that her account of the life and death of Peter Quint is a whopping big "story":

> I scarce know how to put my story into words that shall be a credible picture of my state of mind; but I was in these days literally able to find a joy in the extraordinary flight of heroism the occasion demanded of me.

Even her words "flight of heroism" seemed almost to call for the substitution of the word "imagination" for the word "heroism"!

I remember looking back for earlier indications of her lively imagination, and found at the end of the first chapter that she viewed the big, ugly house as a "castle of romance," remarking to herself: "Wasn't it just a storybook over which I had fallen a-doze and a-dream?" Later, when talking about her pleasure —early in the tale—with the charms of Bly, she says: "Oh, it was a trap—not designed, but deep—to my imagination," going on presently to reveal that imagination at work, telling of the thought "that it would be as charming as a charming story suddenly to meet someone"—the someone, of course, the master who lived on Harley Street, and then, marvel of marvels, being "arrested on the spot" with the sense that her "imagination had, in a flash turned real." It troubled me at the time that the imagined master became the imagined Peter Quint, but I had at least verified to my own satisfaction that her detailed account of the life and death of Peter Quint evolved from the same busy brain—stimulated by long sessions of reading, to satisfy the "curiosity of her youth," about the horrible villainy of mankind. What hadn't she read by the time she worked out the details of Quint's death and the "strange passages and perils, secret disorders, vices more than suspected—that would have accounted for a good deal more"!

In any case, before her eyes are first "unsealed," she had read Ann Radcliffe's *Mysteries of Udolpho,* probably also her *Sicilian Romance* wherein Julia's mother (supposedly dead)

A Stormy Night

lies in a dungeon for fifteen years. Not necessarily, for the presence of an insane or unmentionable relative "kept in unsuspected confinement" is one of the ear-marks of the Gothic novel (see my *Attributes of Gothic*); these incarcerated kin-folk are almost as common as the staunch-if-nervous little heroines. Even Smollett, in his classic but episodic fore-runner, *Ferdinand Count Fathom,* has the mother of Renaldo immured in a "west" tower; and Monk Lewis later embellishes the stock theme with gruesome particulars: hapless creatures surrounded by old mouldy bones and rotting fragments of former victims — even the remains of a baby born in "confinement."

I had to marvel at the skill that sifted such crude material through the governess's "infernal imagination" (as she one time calls it — in the first paragraph of Chapter 13) with a result that is somehow as charming as a charming story over which one may fall a-doze and a-dream. But I was baffled enough — by so many broad hints not elaborated — that when I got up to put another log on the fire, I took down the *Mysteries of Udolpho* and glanced through it. I soon assured myself that the governess uses a much firmer hand with the landscape ecstasies (she is more like James in his travel sketches); and her unexplained noises, blown-out candles, icy blasts, and so on are delicately done. Certainly I found nothing that struck me as even a possible direct source for the governess's account of her experiences at Bly except Madame Cheron's unjust suspicions of her niece, Emily, and her nasty accusations. The governess uses (at times) much the same attitude towards Miles and Flora:

> "I desire you will not walk there again, at so early an hour, unattended," said Madame Cheron: "my gardens are very extensive; and a young woman who can make assignations by moonlight at La Vallée, is not to be trusted to her own inclinations elsewhere."
>
> Emily, extremely surprised and shocked, had scarcely power to beg an explanation of these words; and when she did, her aunt absolutely refused to give it; though, by her severe looks and half sentences, she appeared anxious to impress Emily with a belief that she was well informed of some degrading circumstances of her conduct.

A few pages further on, Madame Cheron really puts the screws

with The Turn of the Screw

on her perfectly innocent niece:

> "Do you know this hand?" said she, in a severe tone, and with a look that was intended to search her heart, while Emily assured her that she did not.
>
> "Do not provoke me," said her aunt: "you do know it: confess the truth immediately. I insist upon your confessing the truth instantly."
>
> Emily was silent and turned to leave the room, but Madame called her back.
>
> "Oh! you are guilty, then!" said she: "you do know the hand."

Of course Madame Cheron is a hypocrite—determined to break up a romance that she thinks would add nothing to her social position. The governess, on the other hand, seems to be genuinely convinced that Miles and Flora see the ghosts. And, at first, she merely thinks about accusing them: "there were times . . . when I would have been ready to swear that . . . they had visitors who were known and were welcome. Then it was that, had I not been deterred by the very chance that such an injury might prove greater than the injury to be averted, my exultation would have broken out. 'They're here, they're here, you little wretches,' I would have cried, 'and you can't deny it now!'" She restrains herself until she and Mrs. Grose (in Chapter 20) find Flora at the lake. Then she accuses her, even though Flora will "not even feign to look in the direction of the prodigy"—accuses her even though she "quails": "my certitude that she thoroughly saw was never greater than at that instant, and in the immediate need to defend myself I called it passionately to witness. 'She's there, you little unhappy thing—there, there, *there,* and you see her as well as you see me!'" When Flora protests, "I don't know what you mean. I see nobody. I see nothing. I never *have.* I think you're cruel. I don't like you!" the governess can only "sadly shake her head" at her and stick to her "miserable truth" that the child does see the ghost of Miss Jessel.

I had another cup of coffee while I cogitated. If the governess did follow Radcliffe's lead with her suspicions and the accusations, she certainly wisely—from the artistic point of view—kept the dear children from making tedious and self-pitying explanations. Miles and Flora are guilty of no such pious monologuing as Emily's:

"Is this, then, the reward of my ingenuousness? . . . the treatment I am to receive from a relation—an aunt—who ought to have been the guardian, not the slanderer of my reputation,—who, as a woman, ought to have respected the delicacy of female honour, and, as a relation should have protected mine! But to utter falsehoods on so nice a subject—to repay the openness, and, I may say with honest pride, the propriety of my conduct, with slanders—required a depravity of heart such as I could scarcely believe existed, such as I weep to find in a relation. Oh, what a contrast does her character present to that of my father! while envy and low cunning form the chief traits of hers, his was distinguished by . . . benevolence and philosophic wisdom! But now let me only remember, if possible, that she is unfortunate."

Chapter III

ON THE ALERT

for other similarities that might prove my case—the nervous governess's imaginative existence *in* a Gothic novel, I browsed some further in *Udolpho,* but I found it so tedious I put it down and simply sat for a while in thought. I don't know how long I meditated, but the storm broke into my reverie with new violence—sparks and ashes spewed from the fireplace as before, the lamp alternately flickered and flared, and a big dead branch rapped with such force on the windowpane that, when another icy gust tore through the house, blowing my papers all everywhere and waking the cat from its curled-up nap on the hearth, I wondered if the pane had been broken. But the window was just as tight as the governess found it at the end of Chapter 17. If the lamp had gone out, I believe I should have expected the cat to tell me, just as Miles told the governess: "It was I who blew it, dear!"

I realized directly that the tearing wind came from the rear of the house. The cat stretched and yawned—quite indifferent to any horrid demonic presence that might have come in with the wind. I made at once for the back of the house, and the cat went right along—sensing the chance to take advantage of someone's going to the kitchen. I was hungry myself. I shut the wide-open door and bolted it. Then I waded through what seemed to be seventeen cats until I had lit a candle and crossed over to the icebox.

But I stood there with my hand on the latch—my action of

A Stormy Night

opening arrested by sudden thought. I had been following a wrong hunch, wrong at least in part; I had been led astray — into supposing James had used the governess as a proxy — by the mere chance of remembering, because of my own feelings alone in the house on a stormy night, his saying: "I am in a Waverly Novel!" The governess raises only two ghosts, hardly enough to people all England, and hers are not characters in fiction, but ghosts of real people — dead servants. Besides, I thought, the whole *Turn of the Screw* is too tall a tale: much of it just as ridiculous as the frozen air coming right through the window and Miles's impish boast that he blew out the candle. That, though, could be called a Radcliffean explaining-away of the supernatural. But it is *too* funny — and the governess ignores the explanation and marches right on with her determinations and preconceived notions. It is also *too* funny that Miles should die of heart-failure in the end, with no preparation for it, no preliminary explaining — as in other stories of James's where a child dies — that he had been delicate from the beginning.

"Aha!" I said to myself, and to the cat who was meowing that I go ahead and open the icebox door. "All right, Cat," I said, lifting the latch; "and I'll tell you a secret if you promise not to tell." I held the milk pitcher a moment in my hand.

"Meow!" said the cat.

"It's simply this," I went on, pouring milk in his bowl and loading his plate with scraps: *"The Turn of the Screw* is in the *Northanger Abbey* tradition!" Then for myself I filled a plate with cold beef, chunks of celery, left-over pudding, and apple pie, and went back to my chair before the fire.

I think it was because my mind was flooded by too many ideas that I went off the track altogether for long enough to think over that old question-answer gag: "How is the art of cooking like the art of love?" "Because the greatest skill is needed in warming over the cold remains." But I liked the beef cold, and the apple pie. Of course I was rather ruefully amused at being such an ass as to jump so fast to a wrong conclusion — with the proofs of *Attributes* right over there on my heaped-up desk, my *History of the Supernatural in the West* in its second

with The Turn of the Screw

edition, and — above all — my article, "Gothic Satire," long since published in *Literature*.

[Exhaustive search has produced *no* information on the several works mentioned; should one, perhaps, suspect a hoax?]

The joke was on me — that I hadn't seen at once that James's "fantastic fiction," his "wanton little bogey-tale," his "shameless potboiler," his *"jeu d'esprit,"* is a farce, a travesty, a satire! [Could our author *possibly* have had access to some of James's correspondence? See *The Letters of Henry James*, ed. Lubbock (New York, 1920), I, 279, 296, 299.] His nervous heroine resembles only too much Jane Austen's Catherine in *Northanger Abbey*, Barrett's absurd "Cherry," and Sarah Green's unbalanced heroine — *also* a parson's daughter — who loses all the sense she ever had by reading too much fiction written expressly for young ladies of extreme sensibility.

[Our author undoubtedly refers to Eaton Stannard Barrett's, *The Heroine, or the Adventures of Cherubina* (1813) and to Sarah Green's *Romance Readers and Romance Writers* (1810).]

No doubt about it. I had been so blind as not to remember that Janie's [*sic!*] Catherine *searches* for horrors just as James's determined governess does. Catherine never finds a skeleton, an immured relative, nor a ghost who can fix her with his awful eyes. But the underlying satirical spirit is the same — though James (naturally) does a whale of a better job — unifying his story and pushing the "joke" to the most horrible, the most "amusing" limit — the absurd death of little Miles.

Well, I ran through the book again, not so much for verification as to see how the trick was played. James had it all thought out ahead of time. His intermediate narrator, Douglas, plants some of the unexciting truths that the novel-devouring governess ignores, distorts, or develops to suit her own taste — her taste for sensational novels where the most innocent-seeming people turn out to be villains of the deepest dye — much as (according to some people) all cats are black at heart.

Douglas makes it clear that she will probably find it dull at Bly, and lonely. She will have to entertain herself as best she can. But Douglas is sly: he presents nothing so banal as an old laundry list for an over-stimulated imagination to transform into a faded manuscript containing the "secret." No. He establishes the thorough respectability of the former governess (later known as Miss Jessel) — a respectability made memorable by some joker's question: "And what did the former governess die of? — of so much respectability?" Although he doesn't mention the valet specifically, Douglas includes him implicitly in the general respectability at Bly — along with an old groom, a housemaid, an old gardener, and — most amazingly — an old pony.

Thus the stage of decorous dull fact is set, and the governess at first follows through — telling how much she expected to be bored. That she is not, is evident enough throughout, but she manages to let it seem at first that her interest lay entirely in the charm of the children: "The attraction of my small charges was a constant joy, leading me to wonder afresh at the vanity of my original fears, the distaste I had begun by entertaining for the probable grey prose of my office. There was to be no grey prose, it appeared, and no long grind; so how could work not be charming that presented itself as daily beauty?" As she continues, one becomes aware that in some ways she is a more knowing young lady than her complaints about her "smothered life" as a poor parson's daughter would indicate: "How can I describe that [the sort of interest her companions inspired] except by saying that instead of growing used to them — and it's a marvel for a governess: I call the sisterhood to witness! I made constant fresh discoveries."

But her interest in the charming children turns to determined conviction that she must protect them — even if she has to invent what it is that she is protecting them from. In her militant search for evil, she leaves no stone unturned — not even a tombstone — and she pressures Mrs. Grose into helping her in the manufacture of spurious scandal. Thus the former governess, vouched for by Douglas as thoroughly respectable, becomes the infamous Miss Jessel — infamous (apparently!) for stooping (for she was a lady) to a love affair with valet Peter Quint — a "base menial" who never wore a hat. Both of them were outrageous, in the eyes of Mrs. Grose and the governess, for the evil practice of going without a hat.

It was obvious to me that Douglas initiated the distinction between the lovely and languid governess-novelist of the pre-

with The Turn of the Screw

amble and the nervous wreck of the tale proper. Neither of these ladies has a name (although Miss Jessel does!) — a most curious oversight for Henry James! Even the servant Luke is dignified with a moniker, to say nothing of the no-character-at-all, Goody Gosling, who had once said something remarkable that the children liked to hear over again. Anyone wise in "Gothic" takes it as a matter of course that the author of an "old manuscript" never misses the chance for increasing authenticity, especially in matters uncanny and mysterious, by using first-person-singular — that vividly seeing and feeling "I."

When Douglas as initiator falls out of the story, a tremendous burden is left on the narrator proper. She it is who must maintain a double picture of things: 1) what is probably the truth and 2) its distortion by that determined parson's daughter in search of excitement, scandal, horror, and evil. Within the tightly circumscribed sphere of first-person narrative she has to present both sides without giving the show away entirely. One might say that the tale she tells shows her own fears of what might have happened to her if she had ever let a roomful of old books get the best of her.

I was naturally curious about what clever woman novelist James had in mind when he thought her — the charmer of the preamble — up. [*It is only by means of the most rigid self-restraint that one can read our author without changing the wording of some of his most outrageous sentences.*] Surely not Jane Austen, nor George Eliot, nor any of the Brontës — none of them could write one half so well. And what the Brontës knew or felt about children — well, Anne wrote about little monsters who cut up live birds gradually, to see how long they would live, who wrestled their governess, spat in her purse, and never, never did their lessons. What shining angels Miles and Flora are by contrast: "They got their little tasks as if they loved them, and indulged . . . in the most unimposed little miracles of memory. They not only popped out at me as tigers and as Romans, but as Shakespeareans, astronomers, and navigators . . . We lived in a cloud of music and love and success and private theatricals." What Anne's sister Charlotte wrote about children is just as damning, but on a different level; what she says bears an astounding resemblance to what the governess

A Stormy Night

in *The Turn of the Screw* imagines about Miles and Flora. Talking about her new place (she is speaking of real children) she says they are not "such incarnate little devils as the Sidgwick's."

> [Our author is slovenly as usual in his scholarship. He seems to refer to *Agnes Grey: A Novel by Acton Bell* and to some collection of the letters of Charlotte Brontë.]

The double picture of Miles and Flora: 1) what they actually say and do — all showing them as good, as real, and as charming as the children Alice Meynell describes in her little book *The Children* (James liked that, praised it highly [*see "London,"* Harper's Weekly, *XLI (Feb. 6, 1897), 135*]— perhaps even thought of her as the type for his lovely lady, and 2) what the impressionable nervous wreck thinks about them, must have been an intricately difficult feat to pull off. [*One cannot avoid annoyance at our author's syntactical license and his disregard for the maintenance of consistency in the usage of levels of diction.*] Even when Miles is what he calls bad — getting up at midnight to scare her into letting him have his way, or blowing out her candle — his pranks are those of a mischievous fairy, Robin Goodfellow or Puck in *Midsummer-Night's Dream*. But it's possible that some readers might be fooled by the governess's intensity into thinking those dear kids *are* incarnate black little devils at heart!

One of the author-governess's most delightful tricks — the one I enjoyed the most on that rereading — is having her invented governess reveal, through her own statements (not with a clumsy omniscient author crowding in to spoil my fun) that she is a "sad case," crazy, insane, deluded, obsessed. She is as "far gone" (to use one of her own revealing expressions) as Janie's Catherine and Sarah Green's daffy preacher's daughter. Sometimes the ironic over-emphasis made me laugh, there by myself in the empty house. I know I broke out over an ironic passage where the governess refers to the children as victims of her "lucidity," and at the seeming innocence of the governess's saying, when Miles plays for her (as she "knew" later, to give Flora a chance for a confab [*ulation*] with Miss Jessel): "David's playing for Saul could never have shown a finer sense of the occasion" — just as though the writer of those lines did not remember that David played to the *mad* Saul, "took a harp,

with The Turn of the Screw

and played with his hand: so Saul was refreshed, and was well, and the evil spirit departed from him" [*I Sam. 16:23*]; but her creator, the novelist-governess, intended that the idea of Saul's madness should get through to the reader. And Saul, I remembered was also a ghost hunter; he persuaded that old spiritualistic medium, the Witch of Endor, to rouse up for a seance the long-dead Samuel [*I Sam. 28: 7-19*]. Oh yes, I thought it was so funny that I laughed and laughed. James out-satired Austen, Barrett, and all the others who made so much fun of the Gothic novel around the turn of the century. But my amusement faded away. I realized I was tired — it was way after midnight. Nagging, unformulated notions were soaking through my consciousness. And questions: why did Miles have to die? There couldn't be any sensible connection between his playing the part of David, for David was old and stricken in years before he slept with his fathers and was buried in the city of David [*I Kings 1: 1; 2: 10*].

Chapter IV

I POURED

myself another cup of coffee, leaned back in the big chair, and shut my eyes. Old Baldy had given me a tough assignment. I'd have to do some serious thinking to come to the definitive conclusion that I knew he expected of me. I had thought it was funny when the governess had fainting fits—like any Gothic heroine, but the David-playing-for-Saul theme brought other whiffs of ancient tradition to my mind. Her descriptions of her thoughts, feelings, sensations before, during, and after her ghostly visions reminded me of old accounts of prophets, saints, monks, and—witches who "saw" things or "heard" voices. For instance, I thought of the other Saul (the one whose name was changed to Paul on his conversion) who "fell to the earth" on the road to Damascus when a light from heaven shone round him and he heard the voice of the Lord [*Acts 9: 3-9*]. I couldn't escape it: there was something about the governess's experiences quite out of gear with the simple fainting fit produced by the crack-brained sensibility that becomes a Gothic heroine. After Mrs. Grose has led away the furious Flora—that child who stubbornly refused to admit she ever "saw" anything—the governess describes her fit (if it is just to call it that) thus: "I only know that at the end of it, I suppose, a quarter of an hour, an odorous dampness and roughness, chilling and piercing my trouble, had made me understand that I must have thrown myself, on my face, on the ground."

Likewise, her sensations *during* an "encounter" appear too circumstantial to be merely funny. She is aware of a silence,

A Stormy Night

a hush; of surroundings "stricken with death," of not being herself "in life"—reminding me of how John of Patmos (among others), when "in the Spirit" (not "in life"), heard behind him a great voice and then had revealed to him all that has been and all that will be when the first heaven and the first earth have passed away. I thought too of that amazing "silence in heaven about the space of half an hour" that takes place on the opening of the seventh seal [*Rev. 8: 1*]. The governess describes her experience of being "not in life," of a silence, a hush, not once only but repeatedly. When she sees Quint on the tower: "I can hear again, as I write, the intense hush in which the sounds of evening dropped. The rooks stopped cawing in the golden sky and the friendly hour lost, for the minute, all its voice." Later, when she sees him on the stairs: "The apparition had reached the landing halfway up. . . . He knew me as well as I knew him; and so, in the cold, faint twilight, with a glimmer in the high glass and another in the polish of the oak stair below, we faced each other in our common intensity. . . . It was the dead silence of our long gaze at such close quarters that gave the whole horror, huge as it was, its only note of the unnatural. If I had met a murderer . . . we . . . would have spoken. Something would have passed, in life, between us. . . . The moment was so prolonged that it would have taken little more to make me doubt if even I were in life. I can't express what followed it save by saying that the silence itself . . . became the element into which I saw the figure disappear."

Even when she has no actual "encounter" herself but merely believes the children have "guests" she experiences a strange stillness. These experiences follow her "secret scenes" shut up in her room where she "audibly rehearsed" what she would say to the children when she made up her mind to accuse them directly. When she joins them she says: "I chattered more than ever, going on volubly enough 'til one of our prodigious, palpable hushes occurred—I can call them nothing else—the strange, dizzy lift or swim (I try for terms!) into a stillness, a pause of all life, that had nothing to do with the more or less noise that at the moment we might be engaged in making and that I could hear through any deepened exhilaration or quick-

with The Turn of the Screw

ened recitation or louder strum of the piano. Then it was the others, the outsiders, were there, . . . causing me . . . to tremble with the fear of their addressing to their younger victims some yet more infernal message or more vivid image than they had thought good enough for myself."

Obviously these descriptions of what she feels and what she thinks is going on are not what one might expect in a satire in the *Northanger Abbey* tradition. They are too accurate, too clinical—as though they require, for fullness of understanding, companion reports (of interest only to the scientifically-minded), like those Dr. Hesselius's medical secretary did *not* publish along with his strange narratives of supernatural experiences.

> [Dr. Martin Hesselius, author of "The Interior Sense and the Conditions of the Opening thereof"; *Mortis Imago* (Essay upon the Drugs of the Dark and Middle Ages); *Essays on Metaphysical Medicine; The Cardinal Function of the Brain;* and of several "stories" included in Joseph Sheridan Le Fanu's *In a Glass Darkly* (London, 1872; reprinted New York, 1929). Is our author unaware that Dr. Hesselius is undoubtedly a product of Le Fanu's imagination?]

It occurred to me that the children were struck much as I was by their governess's sensations, though what they knew of them they got, of course, from her behavior, not from what she tells us. She assumes that they share her "swim into stillness," her "pause of all life": "Such things naturally left on the surface, for the time, a chill which we vociferously denied we felt; and we had, all three, with repetition, got into such splendid training that we went, each time, almost automatically, to mark the close of the incident, through the very same movements. It was striking of the children, at all events, to kiss me inveterately with a kind of wild irrelevance and never to fail— one or the other—of the precious question that had helped us through many a peril. 'When do you think he *will* come? Don't you think we *ought* to write?'—there was nothing like that inquiry, we found by experience, for carrying off an awkwardness. 'He' of course was their uncle in Harley Street."

What did the sympathetic children suppose was happening to their governess in these repeated "incidents"? Was she having fits—epileptic or otherwise? Why the uncle from "Harley

§ 23 §

A Stormy Night

Street" if not to minister to a young woman in poor health? In the preamble, Douglas describes that uncle as living in a house unnecessarily "vast and imposing" for a bachelor, a man "bold and pleasant, offhand and gay and kind," who had "charming ways with women." I confess I toyed with the idea that Bly, that "country home," was simply a retreat for harmless lunatics and that the governess, according to established custom, had fallen in love with her alienist.

> [Perhaps our author was led into this idea by reading another of Le Fanu's works, *The Rose and the Key*, 3 vols. (London, 1871), which deals with the horrors of a private insane asylum?]

Mrs. Grose, too, it occurred to me, in spite of her complicity in twisting simple facts to their worst possible construction, seems often moved with compassion for what strikes her as at least an affliction if not downright madness. The governess remarks: "I could feel her, when she surveyed them . . .thank the Lord's mercy that if they were ruined the pieces would still serve. . . I had already begun to perceive how, with the development of the conviction that — as time went on without a public accident — our young things could . . . look out for themselves, she addressed her greatest solicitude to the sad case presented by their instructress." I couldn't laugh any more at the irony of the governess's referring to herself as a "sad case."

> [Again it is possible to observe that our author is not familiar with, or at least did not utilize, the New York Edition of *The Novels and Tales* or he would have been cognizant of the fact that James replaced the word "instructress" with "deputy-guardian" (XII, 231).]

Chapter V

BUT I HATED

to believe it that the governess was crazier than Catherine and Cherubina. I took up the book again and set myself the task of looking for things that I *could* laugh at. I forced a chuckle at the governess's retort—when Mrs. Grose intimates that indeed it is time to send for the master if the house is poisoned and the children mad: "If I am myself, you mean?" And I smiled—albeit wryly, at the humor of: "I had made her a receptacle of lurid things, but there was an odd recognition of my superiority . . . in her patience under my pain. She offered her mind to my disclosures as, had I wished to mix a witch's broth and proposed it with assurance, she would have held out a large clean saucepan." To anyone with my background, of course, a witch is madder than a March Hare, a Mad Hatter, or an eighteenth-century parson's daughter who confuses fact and fiction. Indoctrinated by Reginald Scot and the other brave spirits who dared the displeasure of their sovereigns by declaring a war of words on the too-long-prolonged human insanity or viciousness that burned thousands of crazy old women (and young ones too) at the stake because they "confessed" to ridiculous and impossible offenses —having "carnal copulation" with the devil or his henchmen, or murdering an enemy at a distance by sending the tabby cat, the toad, or the pet mole to do the job—I couldn't be amused at the idea that the governess was a "witch." Nor could I be amused that she fancied herself as a screen between the children and the evil ghosts, as their well-intentioned "savior."

Besides, the picture of Mrs. Grose as the receptacle, the large

A Stormy Night

clean saucepan, brought to my mind the great gullible public that gulped down eagerly the "witch's broth" concocted less by the crazy witches themselves than by their persecutors—officers of church or state or both. They kept the public in line, and they prompted the victims—telling them what *to* confess. With the *Malleus Maleficarum* (prepared expressly for the purpose) as authority and guide, it was easy enough to tell an unwanted person, a suspected "witch," what crimes he was guilty of, and yes, convince him too—by stretching him a little further on the rack or giving another turn to the thumbscrew—that he had done impossible things. Those who refused to confess, or who held out the longest, were supposedly supported in spirit by their guardian devil who made it possible for them to endure the strain, the pressure, and the pain—both physical and mental. But confessions came at last when the misery became too intense for man or woman (or guardian devil) to endure. It is this traditional sustaining evil spirit that the governess seems to have in mind (in the last chapter) when she springs straight upon Miles, for "there again, against the glass, as if to blight his confession and stay his answer, was the hideous author of our woe—the white face of damnation." It interested me that her concept of the ghost's function had shifted from her earlier notion that he had come into view "like a sentinel before a prison." In fact, I was confused: was Peter Quint a good spirit or an evil one—that is, as the governess imagined him: I couldn't believe in him myself.

I didn't like the confused turn my thoughts were taking. How far I had strayed from my earlier notions—that James was peopling all England with ghosts, that the governess was *in* a Gothic novel, whether in a serious or a satirical way, that— well, what all else had I thought? I was about in the same fix as the governess when she says to Mrs. Grose: "The more I go over it, the more I see in it, and the more I see in it the more I fear. I don't know what I *don't* see—what I *don't* fear!" Or I was like all seven of the blind men who described the elephant as like a rope, like a tree, like a wall, like a fan, and so on, and like them too in not being able to put my humpty-dumpty together. What, by all that's holy, I thought, am I going to do about a critique for good old Baldy Twitchell? He would want a

with The Turn of the Screw

dignified article—neat, definitive, conclusive—no conjectures, all demonstrable fact. Well, I'd either put him off with an excuse or dash off some positive little fib ("delicious little horror tale") that wouldn't trick me into admitting that I had not only too many ideas but also too many questions. These random questions hit me from time to time like the shots of a nearly petered-out military engagement. And some I still can't answer.

Chapter VI

BUT SOMETIMES ANSWERS

came to questions I didn't know I had asked myself. For instance, when I sat there staring at the fire, burned down to a bed of glowing coals with the two polished brass knobs of the andirons standing a-glitter in front of them as if on guard, I was reminded of Dr. Hesselius and his subtle trick of putting something shiny (but nothing so obvious as a coin or a watch) in front of the person whose "interior sense" is about to be opened and whose inner eye unsealed. Not that Dr. Hesselius made any point of it—he simply had the shiny thing there: a silver tray, brass nailheads on a sedan chair, or a streak of last-minute light from the setting sun shining through a crack. And in one case (the one about the bachelor-vicar tormented by the red-eyed monkey), the demonic creature vanishes (though he always comes back after letting the poor vicar have a little rest) into a bed of glowing coals that gradually fade away—not real coals such as I faced, but imaginary or "seen" coals that appear spontaneously on a cold hearth. (A neat trick—if one could get the knack of it!) These glowing or shining objects of Dr. Hesselius's reminded me of the "glimmer in the high glass and another on the polish of the oak stair below" when the governess and the "figure" on the stairs face each other in "common intensity." And of the governess's eyes so attached to her stitching—or to her thimble a-glitter in "the brightness of the hot still hour"—that she "can feel once more the spasm of an effort not to move them."

I was annoyed; I even muttered to myself: "Get thee behind

A Stormy Night

me, Dr. Hesselius!" And I told him that the scene is just as remindful of Adeline in *The Romance of the Forest* when she doesn't dare raise her eyes to the glass for fear she will see reflected there somebody else's face. But the more I stared at the coals, the more I saw, and the more I saw, the more I feared that the governess was the victim of a Svengali or that she suffered from spontaneous self-hypnosis. What was it about needlework, and where had I seen it—surely I could find it in my notes (for my next projected work: on the relationship between ancient interpretations of visions, talismans and mental therapy, dreams, somnambulism, epilepsy, amnesia—all that kind of thing). But I kept on staring at the glowing coals, hoping I would remember, without having to search through a real mess of unclassified scribbles.

[One is aghast at such an admission of slovenly procedure in the taking of notes! Perhaps the reason no trace of the "projected work" can be discovered is—to put it concretely—that "the real mess" was *never* sorted and classified.]

And I *did* remember. Myers makes some mention of it when talking about Dr. Azam's famous Felida X., and so does Breuer in his case of—what was the woman's name?—his one case anyway in the joint work of Breuer and Freud, *Studien über Hysterie*.

[German ed., 1895; trans. by James Strachey as *Studies on Hysteria* (New York, 1957); our author refers to the case history of Fräulein Anna O., pp 21-47. He would have done well to search his notes or read the case history over again, for no reference to "needlework" appears in Strachey's translation of the case mentioned except a reference to the patient's becoming confused about colors because in 1881 "she had been very busy with a dressing-gown for her father, which was made with the same material as her present dress, but was blue instead of brown" (p. 34). Earlier, however, in the "Preliminary Communication," written in collaboration by Breuer and Freud, may be found the following: "We have nothing new to say on the question of the origin of these dispositional hypnoid states. They often, it would seem, grow out of the day-dreams which are so common even in healthy people and to which *needlework* and similar occupations render women especially prone" (p. 13).]

I stared at the glowing coals for clarification of my thoughts, but presently I got up (feeling myself beginning to doze), poured another cup of coffee, and walked around, both to wake

with The Turn of the Screw

up and to find the books I was thinking of. The *Studien* I must have lent to someone; I couldn't find the book, nor have I seen it since. But soon I was back in my chair with Myers' *Human Personality and Its Survival of Bodily Death*—a curious mixture of cautious science and superstitious wishful-thinking. The coffee was bitter medicine, but it woke me up. Felida X., the classic case of double personality, exhibited symptoms of hysteria as early as thirteen. She would suddenly fall asleep and wake up in ten minutes or so with an entirely different personality. In her primary state she was industrious and rational. Almost every day what she called her *crise* came on spontaneously—"often while she was sitting at her needlework"—preceded by a brief interval of profound sleep from which no external stimulus could rouse her. When she did wake up, she was a different person—happy and gay instead of melancholy as she was in her "primary state." Breuer's case was much the same, but, as I recall, that young lady was cured by falling into self-hypnosis every day, and then, with Breuer at hand to assist, telling him her troubles. In other cases he and Janet and countless others before them performed their miraculous cures by means of suggestion under hypnosis; this young woman, a Fraulein Somebody, could hypnotize herself—and thus she was Freud's great incentive; he admitted he was not successful as a hypnotist, but, inspired by Breuer's amazing young woman, he invented his pressure system—making his patients talk and talk while he pressed them on the head. Sooner or later they came through with the kind of information he wanted. Of course the pressure system was merely a modification of stock methods of inducing hypnosis. Staring at a shiny object (Braid's method) was a favorite—and probably still is. But any method of forcing concentration to the point of exhaustion would work (or so the authorities said)—even the business of a "mutual fixed stare," with the doctor standing over the patient so the patient would get tired faster by having to look up. It occurred to me that by staring *down* at Quint on the stairs the governess was thus able, by turning the tables, to get the best of him and make him disappear into the "element" of silence.

It was all very confusing to me. She seems at times to act

A Stormy Night

the part of the hypnotist and at other times to hypnotize herself—or to be acting on suggestions made to her earlier by somebody else (but *who*?). I had to race through the book again to get a clearer comprehension of my own ideas. Certainly in connection with her "needlework" I found a remarkable correlation—if not a clean-cut cause-and-effect relationship, between her sewing or knitting and her strange powers of seeing things or of knowing that ghostly creatures are present. First of all, but scarcely to be noticed except in the light of later experiences, she puts "three stitches" in her gloves not long before she sees Quint at the window in Chapter 4. Two chapters later, when she visits the "Sea of Azof" with Flora, her repeated references to her eyes more than suggest that her concentration on the "piece of work," the "stitching," brings about her "secondary state" (as the psychologists call it). But the issue is confused by her mentioning "the small click" that would tick out "the right second" for her to look up: she may be self-hypnotized, but at the same time she is behaving as though acting on post-hypnotic sugestion—and timing it exactly right too for the astonishment of all observers. And yet—I confess I was confused—the whole passage may be read quite simply, with the details about her eyes and her stitching having no bearing on her "condition":

> Suddenly . . . I became aware that . . . we had an interested spectator. The way this knowledge gathered in me was the strangest thing in the world—the strangest, that is, except the very much stranger in which it quickly merged itself. I had sat down with a piece of work—for I was something or other that could sit—on the old stone bench which overlooked the pond; and in this position I began to take in with certitude, and yet without direct vision, the presence, at a distance, of a third person. The old trees, the thick shrubbery, made a great and pleasant shade, but it was all suffused with the brightness of the hot, still hour. There was no ambiguity in anything; none whatever, at least, in the conviction I from one moment to another found myself forming as to what I should see straight before me and across the lake as a consequence of raising my eyes. They were attached at this juncture to the stitching in which I was engaged, and I can feel once more the spasm of my effort not to move them till I should so have steadied myself as to be able to make up my mind what to do. There was an alien figure in view—a figure whose right of presence I instantly, passionately questioned . . . Of the positive identity of the appar-

with The Turn of the Screw

ition I would assure myself as soon as the small clock of my courage should have ticked out the right second; meanwhile, with an effort that was already sharp enough, I transferred my eyes straight to little Flora, who at the moment, was about ten yards away.

Before she gets the courage to shift her eyes again, she is aware of a silence, a hush, that makes the whole incident like the others when she feels she is "not in life" — an abeyance of one sense that (as the authorities repeatedly say) takes place under hypnosis while the patient (or victim?) concentrates on the hallucinations formed by another sense. Breuer's Fraulein, for instance, became deaf when she saw snakes or the terrifying vision of her father with a death's head.

[Our author as usual is careless with his particulars and with his references. There is no essential concomitancy between Fräulein Anna O.'s deafness and her terrifying visions. Also it may be noted that he puts a scholar to unnecessary search by not giving the full name of the authorities he mentions. "Myers," for instance, is Frederic W. H. Myers, a great Wordsworthian who won prizes for Latin lyrics and was probably the first Englishman ever to swim across the river below Niagara Falls; he was an essayist on such varied subjects as Virgil and *Science and a Future Life* (1893), as well as "the leading spirit of the small band of men who in 1882 . . . founded the Society for Psychical Research," of which he, as well as William James, was, at one time, president. The *Human Personality* (referred to by our author) appeared posthumously in two large volumes in 1903 with many long quotations from the *Proceedings* of S.P.R. In the subsequent one-volume abridged edition (London, 1919) many of the quotations are omitted. For the "needlework" reference see the 1919 ed., pp. 40-41, where Myers quotes from Dr. A. Binet's *Altérations de la Personalité* (pp. 6-20) some portions of Dr. Azam's original report on Felida X. "Braid" is James Braid, author of *Neurypnology, or the Rationale of Nervous Sleep* (1843); he is commonly called the "father of hypnotism" because he gave a new name to the phenomenon earlier known as "mesmerism," "somnambulism," etc. His *Neurypnology* has recently been made easily available by J. H. Conn, M.D., of the Johns Hopkins Medical School under the title of *Braid on Hypnotism* (New York, 1960). Our author is inexcusably negligent in overlooking the chapter on hypnotism in William James *The Principles of Psychology*, 2 vols. (New York, 1890); 2 vols. in one (New York, 1950), II, 593-616.]

But — to get back to the "needlework" — late in the tale (in Chapter 23) the governess gives it away that there *is* a close

A Stormy Night

relationship between her "work" and her peculiar states of unusual awareness of strange matters. As she tells it, she hides behind her "work" to conceal her nervousness, and has done so *repeatedly* — apparently unaware that her concentration may cause her hallucinations and unfounded convictions: "He [Miles] remained there awhile, with his forehead against the glass, in contemplation of the stupid shrubs I knew and the dull things of November. I had always my hypocrisy of 'work,' behind which, now, I gained the sofa. Steadying myself with it there as I had repeatedly done at those moments of torment that I have described as the moments of my knowing the children to be given to something from which I was barred, I sufficiently obeyed my habit of being prepared for the worst. But an extraordinary impression dropped on me as I extracted a meaning from the boy's embarrassed back — none other than that I was not barred now. This inference grew in a few minutes to sharp intensity and seemed bound up with the direct perception that it was positively *he* who was." Apparently she keeps up her concentrated hypocrisy of work throughout the chapter; in the next to last paragraph she says, "I achieved thoughtfully a few loops of my knitting," and at the end of the chapter, when she is asking Miles to tell her a "mere fraction of the whole" of the truth, she intersperses: "oh, my work preoccupied me, and I was off-hand!" Directly thereafter, in the beginning of the last chapter, she imagines that Peter Quint comes into view at the window. What happens in that chapter is not easy to face: hypnotized, whether by herself or by the earlier-implanted suggestions of a Svengali, the governess behaves in such a way that Miles dies — just how, I could not understand, but he dies. Naturally, I thought of the many long arguments about whether a person could be induced by post-hypnotic suggestion to commit a crime; authorities differ, some saying it is impossible, that the hypnotized subject is always sufficiently aware to avoid doing anything contrary to his own conscience. Others are convinced of rapes and seductions, and make plausible conjectures about murders.

I didn't dwell on the idea, but it led me to another, a question: was *The Turn of the Screw* after all a satire, not on the Gothic novel so much as on *all* the thinking of the Gay Nineties on

with The Turn of the Screw

unexplained phenomena—covering the whole range of scientific psychologists, persons frankly superstitious, and those in the middle ground, men like Myers, Podmore, and Gurney—not to mention Henry James's brother William who never could make up his mind?

[Concerning William James's indecisiveness, see *William James on Psychical Research,* ed. Gardner Murphy and Robert O. Ballou (New York, 1960).]

Chapter VII

WHEN I EXAMINED

the conditions preceding the governess's other "absences," I found evidence — even if hazy — that she exposes herself to one or another of the established techniques for inducing hypnosis: staring at something, listening to music or to the ticking of a watch, and so on. It was obvious that day-dreaming and expectancy brings on the hallucination of the ghost of Peter Quint on the tower, and that a similar expectancy unseals her eyes for a glimpse of Miss Jessel seated on the lower steps, "her body half bowed and her head, in an attitude of woe, in her hands." And this time the governess quite unnecessarily gives it away that she is familiar with the importance of the hypnotist's looking down while the subject looks up: "I wondered whether, if instead of being above I had been below, I should have had, for going up, the same nerve I had lately shown Quint." Likewise, when she discovers Miles on the lawn looking up, she assumes that "he stood there motionless, and *as if fascinated [italics our author's]*, looking up . . . at something that was apparently above me." For a sheltered parson's daughter, I thought, she knows too much; she has been earlier hypnotized by *some*body — most likely by the master, the "uncle" of the children. She had learned the fundamentals there in Harley Street with that fascinating master who had "charming ways with women." Early in the tale she admits to Mrs. Grose: "I'm rather easily carried away. I was carried away in London." It is this "master" whom she hopes to meet "at the turn of the path," expecting him to "smile and approve."

A Stormy Night

But why does he turn into a figure who is like "nobody"? Why does he become that red-headed horror, Peter Quint?

Suddenly, like the governess herself, I *knew*, I *knew!* She was being "cured" by a clever hypnotist, cured of an unrequited love by a technique made famous by one of the Frenchmen — not Charcot but one of the Janets, probably Pierre. I started to get up to look for all the Janet papers, but I happily remembered that Myers, in his usual fair-minded way, mentions the clever deceit for aiding the love-lorn. And I had Myers right beside me. But I didn't find the passage as fast as I expected; I wasted time reading over such stuff [*sic!*] as: "There are in hysteria frequent *acquisitions* as well as *losses* of faculty. It is not unusual to find great hyperæsthesia in certain special directions — of touch, hearing, perception of light, etc. — combined with hysterical loss of sensation of other kinds" [*op. cit.*, p. 43] — a bit of documentation it would be well for me to keep in mind if I ever got around to writing for Baldy Twitchell the careful scholarly paper he wanted. Clever logician, that Myers — working around to what he considered carefully weighed proof of telepathy, and proceeding from there to "proof" of the reasonableness of communication with discarnate spirits. I found myself laughing again — *The Turn of the Screw* could certainly be taken as a satire on the whole mix-up: ghosts, discarnate spirits, hallucinations — who *could* say? — and if hallucinations, self-induced, post-hypnotic, spontaneously somnambulistic, or simply insane?

At last I found what I was after: "In certain cases of Janet's, indeed, a new and false, but helpful memory was substituted for the old distressing memory; as where a hysteric suffering from horror at the recollection of having been made to sleep as a child along with another child suffering from a skin-disease, was persuaded by hypnotic suggestion that this other child had really been perfectly well." I read on, expecting to find the reference to Titania, but Myers — in *his* kind of orderly way — had put that in the back of the book:

> Dr. Janet finds that hypnotic suggestion, — used with great patience and tact, is able gradually to remove a great number of these mental spasms and insistent memories. It is not, of course, enough to make a suggestion crudely and bluntly. In order to make it *take*, it must be grafted adroitly upon the

with The Turn of the Screw

patient's mental condition of the moment. First of all, one must discover the hidden sources of her trouble—of which sources, strangely enough, she is often herself unaware—and then one must gradually suggest successive slight modifications in the painful memory. "The incident which gave you the shock was not so bad as you think; it really happened thus and thus," says Dr. Janet, until at last the old horror is forgotten, or transformed into something grotesque or innocuous.

Thus one patient is led to believe that the haunting word "cholera" is really the name of a Chinese general; another, who has loved not wisely, but too well, is induced to see the lover of her hallucinatory memories with head transformed into a pig's, and undergoes a revulsion of feeling, *à la* Titania [see the 1903 ed. of *Human Personality*, I, 56, 298-299].

That was all. I had expected more particulars, more cases, especially the case where a red-headed repulsive creature is substituted for the loved image—but that was somewhere in Janet himself. I had enough to satisfy me—if not old Baldy.

[The detailed information, or some of it, that our author refers to may be found in English in Pierre Janet, *Psychological Healing: A Historical and Clinical Study*, 2 vols. (London, 1925), I, 352-353:

In the cases frequently encountered in which the somnambulism is only the expression of a regret or of an unhappy love experience, I have availed myself of the power of suggestion to modify the face of the well-beloved, the face which the subject was continually calling up in imagination. I have equipped this face with carroty hair, with an absurdly misshapen nose, or with some other characteristic repulsive to the subject; and I have often been surprised how powerful was the effect of such transformations upon these persons whose minds are simple and credulous.—Ap. (f., 26), with a history of having had somnambulistic crises eight years earlier, had been abandoned by her lover. For eight months she had been subject to almost daily attacks of delirium in which she saw this lost lover, talked to him, caressed him for several hours. She was amazed at the transformations I effected in the dream image, became rather indignant, and wanted to go on loving it; but she could not succeed, and was completely cured in six weeks.—I could quote a dozen instances of the same kind. In other cases, the trouble took the form of remorse or terror, but could be similarly transformed.—Dz. a young woman of twenty-three, had been terribly frightened, on opening the door of a cupboard, to see within a mounted skeleton, was greatly alarmed by it, talked to it, fancied she was struggling with it, and so on. I was able to rid her of her skeleton in three sittings.

Evidently our author overlooked the obvious fact that the young

A Stormy Night

woman who was terrified of the skeleton is just as pertinent to his general thesis as the young woman induced to imagine "carroty" hair on the object of her misguided affections.]

My own case, though, it seemed to me, was getting desperate; I would have to give up on any neat, conclusive, scholarly piece; I'd have to keep to myself the amazing news that Henry James has written the most ambiguous little novel that the world has ever seen. (The funniest thing — at that time I didn't know more than the half of it!) I realized, of course that the governess's "lucidity" is that of the "lucid somnambulist" — a fashion in mental healing started, as best I could remember, by Puységur about 1800 when he "magnetized" a country lout who woke up with more intelligence than he had before — thus starting a fashion for finding lost gold or determining the proper cure for a disease, by employing the remarkable "lucidity" of certain privileged persons.

> [Our author, in this instance, rather underplays the situation; as Janet *(op. cit.,* I, 33-59, 190, *passim.)* describes the furor: this induced "intellectual exaltation," this remarkable "lucidity," was worked on for half a century by "able investigators" who strove to "render the somnambulists more 'lucid' than ever"; even the newspapers (in advertisements) contained "puffs of somnambulists, described as 'lucid,' 'very lucid,' or 'ultra-lucid,' according to the fees demanded." The fashion was even dramatized on the stage, the mystery unravelled by young women in the "lucid" state; and Leonie, Janet's own most famous case, had been a "lucid somnambulist" in her youth.]

My good humor came back to me; I could really laugh again, and heartily, at the passage where the governess refers to the children as the "victims" of her "lucidity":

> " . . . but even while they pretend to be lost in their fairy-tale they're steeped in their vision of the dead restored. He's not reading to her," I declared; "they're talking of *them* — they're talking horrors! I go on, I know, as if I were crazy; and it's a wonder I 'm not. What I've seen would have made *you* so; but it has only made me more lucid, made me get hold of still other things."
>
> My lucidity must have seemed awful, but the charming creatures who were victims of it, passing and repassing in their interlocked sweetness, gave my colleague something to hold on by; and I felt how tight she held as, without stirring in the breath of my passion, she covered them still with her eyes.

The most gratifying thing about my new discoveries — satire on

with The Turn of the Screw

the conflicting attitudes of the period about young women who see things—was that they did not conflict with my earlier ideas of a Gothic heroine steadfastly, bravely, ridiculously marching through a satirical Gothic novel.

Chapter VIII

BELIEVING I HAD SOLVED

the problem, I thought of going to bed, but the fire was too good to walk off on. And I had planned to make a night of it. Besides, I had soaked up so much coffee I knew I wouldn't get a wink — I'd just lie there wide-eyed and twitch. I laid a couple of fresh logs on the andirons and shoveled coals and half-burnt ends of sticks on top. As I squatted there, listening to the crackle of wood beginning to catch fire and waiting to see the first spurt of flame burst up through the shuddering smoke, I noticed how quiet it was — no more wild wind howling to come in, no more pounding of branches on the windowpane — only now and then the gentle tapping of a twig as though a polite "ghost" were saying "please." Then an idea suddenly came to me: my "interior sense," as it were, was opened again. Not that I relinquished the idea that a therapeutic hypnotist had convinced Titania-the-governess that her beloved had the face of a red-headed pig. But I "saw" who that pig, that base menial Peter Quint, was — I saw the underlying meaning, the truth of the man.

He was a tutor but not a gentleman — son of a peasant or a shopkeeper; not English, but French; so his name was Pierre. He had in his charge a young boy who was devoted to him. They were inseparables — off on long rambles together, intimate — all this long ago, between the American and French Revolutions. I had read the story in an old magazine when I was nineteen or twenty — lying belly-bumper [sic] on the floor of my grandmother's attic (where she kept all manner of stuff

A Stormy Night

that "someone might find a use for some day"). That strange scorched smell peculiar to attics was all around me—even entering into the story in an odd way and making it smell of the past—of those long-ago times when a "lady" could not fall in love with a "base menial" without being called horrible names by her aristocratic class-conscious brother. I couldn't remember the title, but I did remember that Henry James had written it.

So I had come full circle! I was back where I had started—with James digging up ghosts from the fiction of the past and putting them in *The Turn of the Screw*! And ghosts from a fiction of his own! Peter Quint and Miss Jessel reincarnated, in a dim way, Pierre (I could not remember his last name) and the boy's aunt who had been his governess; she had taught him to read before the tutor. The tutor and the governess-aunt had fallen in love—with the boy as a witness to the developing affair. It was the boy (but speaking as an old man, an old baron remembering his childhood) who told the story.

Watching the fire take hold and blaze high, I wished I could remember more details. The governess-aunt had been hideously suspected by her class-conscious brother—just as Emily had been suspected by Madame Cheron, and Quint and Miss Jessel by the governess—with the pressured assistance of Mrs. Grose. Ha, I thought, that incessant pressuring of Mrs. Grose resembles Freud's pressuring of recalcitrant patients, pressure sustained or repeated until they told him exactly what he wanted to know! That is, at those times when her persistent quizzing doesn't more nearly resemble what Lodge called "fishing."

[See the *Proceedings* S.P.R., VI, 448-453, and Myers, *op.cit.* (1903), II, 604-605, in regard to the Dr. Phinuit of Mrs. Piper: "... the utilisation of trivial indications, of every intimation, audible, tactile, muscular, and of little shades of manner too indefinable to name; all these excited in the sitter by skillful guesses and well-directed shots, and their nutriment exacted by superhuman cunning ... At times Dr. Phinuit does fish. Occasionally he guesses; and sometimes he ekes out the scantiness of his information from the resources of a lively imagination. Whenever his supply of information is abundant there is no sign of the fishing process. At other times it is as if he were in a difficult position—only able to gain information from very indistinct or inaudible

with The Turn of the Screw

sources, and yet wishful to convey as much information as possible." Dr. Phinuit, it may be said, was Mrs. Piper's "spirit-control" in her world-famous seances.]

But the French lovers were vindicated: it came out that the governess-aunt and the tutor were as thoroughly respectable as everyone at Bly—even the old pony.

As I watched the fire roaring into magnificent blaze, it occurred to me that that old magazine—an *Atlantic*, as I remembered—might be up in my so-called "study" where a lot of possibly-useful-someday stuff in my grandmother's attic had been stored at the time of her death. I should go see. But I waited, lazy I guess, and contented, watching the flames reach higher and higher into the soot-blackened throat of the chimney. The cat was sitting up, solemnly watching too. "As big as a blazing fire," I remarked to the cat. I realized the next moment that I was quoting a bit of nonsense—the foolish words the governess shrieks when she tries desperately to open the sealed eyes of Mrs. Grose and make her see the "livid predecessor," that "pale and ravenous demon," across the lake—a demon earlier and consistently described as in mournful black. What thing "as big as a blazing fire" does the governess "see" this time? The Angel of the Lord in the burning bush? Miss Jessel suffering the torments of the damned in hell? Or a medieval witch suffering the torments of those damned by the Inquisition? Was I reading into the governess's senseless comparison a more subtle implication than the silliness of it called for?

I gave a log such a kick that the sparks flew upward in a shower. It annoyed me that I had interrupted myself again. Why hadn't I gone right upstairs looking for that old *Atlantic* when I first thought about it? Without more ado, I took up a candle, lit it, and headed for the stairs.

Of course the candle went out before I reached the first landing—I was taking the steps two at a time. I thought it easier from there on to feel my way rather than bother with lighting the candle again—maybe over and over again.

"Now then, Peter Quint," I muttered, "I'll catch up with you. Not necessarily here on the stairs, but up there in that unused room!" With my hand on the banister I had no other trouble in

A Stormy Night

my ascent. I even sniggered over the rare chance of meeting Peter Quint in the flesh—and again at having said it wrong; a discarnate spirit has no flesh. I wondered how people *do* feel when their eyes are unsealed and they believe in their supposedly buried Caesars, their Banquos, and "Is this a dagger that I see before me?" I turned corners with the efficiency of a blind man and made it up to the third floor. Odd thing, I thought, that most of the ghosts seen in drama are guilt-complex ghosts or revenge ghosts or both, but those in the *Proceedings* and in Myers seem to have little reason for their return. Those the governess "sees" are like the ones in Myers—they don't do anything except appear, not even as her prejudiced account presents them; their evil potentialities are all in her imaginings or like the Asiatic goblins who steal children, or Irish fairies—like those in Le Fanu's story where the mother at the end of the tale calls to her remaining children: "Come here and sit on my knee . . . and I'll hold you fast that none can take yez from me."

[See "The Child that went with the Fairies," *All the Year Round* (Feb. 5, 1870). The 1870 date, it should seem, is significant; did our author read this story also while lying *prone* on the floor of his grandmother's attic? It was not reprinted until 1923; see *Madam Crowl's Ghost and Other Tales of Mystery*, ed. M. R. James (London, 1923).]

Continuing to feel my way, I counted doors as I passed down the long hall, hoping my guess was right, that the "study" was the sixth after the turn to the left. But I was soon so mixed up that I didn't know where I was. I struck a match to get my bearings and saw—imagine my surprise, I, a life-long skeptic!—saw two flaming eyes staring right at me, fixing me, holding me for a hideous long moment in terrible, silent communication. The match burned down to my fingers and guttered out. I felt something rub against me and heard a strange breathing. I recognized it a moment later as purring. "Damn you, Cat!" I said, giving him a shove with my foot; "there's nothing to eat up here, unless it's mice, and I know you're too infernal [*ly*] lazy to catch one."

I found the "study" after a few more matches and hasty glances into wrong rooms, lit the candle, looked around at the stacked boxes of books and papers I had never found time to

with The Turn of the Screw

unpack. Taken in by the sunshine streaming in through the high-up windows one bright morning of early spring, I had dubbed that room my study; but I soon gave up trying to use it: when the trees and vines leafed out it was too dark; in the winter, without a fireplace, too cold and dreary. Bookshelves, desk, chair, and lamp had long awaited my return. The lamp gurgled when I gave it a shake. So I rubbed the dusty chimney on my pants and lit the thing. A lopsided flame elongated itself into a smoky streak, but it would serve my purpose, of finding that old *Atlantic,* better than a candle. I glanced first at the bookshelves, but soon I was tearing into boxes, stacking and unstacking, getting numb in my legs from so much squatting around, breathless from so much lifting and shoving, and, I may confess, at intervals disgusted with myself for thumbing through some book that had nothing to do with my business.

At last—to get on—I found the *Atlantic* for September 1869, and yes, there was the story; I recognized the title as soon as I saw it: "Gabrielle de Bergerac"—the name of the governess-aunt of the little boy. Sitting on a box I started reading: "A week after this memorable visit to Fossy, in emulation of my good preceptor, I treated my friends, or myself at least, to a five minutes' fright. Wandering beside the river one day when Coquelin had been—" That was the base-menial tutor's name, Coquelin—Pierre Coquelin. I tried, but couldn't quite, pronounce "Coquelin" so it would sound like "Quint." What I had was the third installment. I soon found the August number, but the July apparently was in some other box or lost. Thinking I'd hunt for it (or know I wouldn't need it) before I went downstairs, I sat down at the desk to look over the two I had.

The second part begins with a description of how the boy and his tutor spend a hot dry summer lazing around on the river bank, taking long walks—inseparable companions, just as I had remembered. I put checkmarks by the passages I might want to copy later:

> He gave me in the course of these walks a great deal of good advice; and without perverting my signorial morals or instilling any notions that were treason to my rank and position, he kindled in my childish breast a little democratic flame which has never quite become extinct . . . Later in life I might have found him too

A Stormy Night

rigorous a moralist; but in those days I liked him all the better for letting me sometimes feel the curb.

What a wholesome relationship between man and boy! Of course I was delighted to be reassured about the unquestionable respectability of the little boy, his tutor, and his governess-aunt.

When the boy tired of fishing or they ran out of things to talk about those long summer days, Coquelin told him stories: "he would lie there with his thumb in his book and his eyes half closed and tell me fairy-tales till the eyes of both of us closed together." How Mrs. Grose and the governess, had they been there to watch, would have disapproved! Mrs. Grose would have reminded the boy that *she* "liked to see young gentlemen not forget their station"; and the governess would have said to Mrs. Grose: "Even while they pretend to be lost in their fairy-tale they're steeped in their vision of the dead restored . . . They're talking of *them* — they're talking horrors!"

Of course I didn't read straight through — not in that cold room, but glanced here and there. It's near the end that the notion of the boy's being corrupted by the tutor comes out, and it's his father who functions as virtuous critic almost eager to read evil into innocence (à la Madame Cheron in *Udolpho* and the governess-housekeeper combination at Bly): "The next time you go on your adventures," says the boy's father to his sister, "I'd thank you not to pollute my son by dragging him at your skirts." He has already called her "Coureuse!" and later he reveals the gist of his earlier hideous assumption that she has besmirched the baronial name: "Gabrielle, the long and short of it appears to be that after all you needn't marry this man." Aha, I thought, here I have the very nub of the resemblance: Mrs. Grose may be understood to imply that Miss Jessel similarly failed, in her evil passion for a "nobody," to maintain her pride in the "propriety of her conduct." The good housekeeper is not so direct as the old baron, perhaps only half-believing what has been pressured out of her by the governess, and so saying something, almost anything, to make the governess let her alone:

"Then you do know what she died of?" I asked.

"No — I know nothing. I wanted not to know; I was glad enough I didn't; and I thanked heaven she was well out of this!"

with The Turn of the Screw

"Yet you had, then, your idea—"
"Of her real reason for leaving? Oh, yes—as to that. She couldn't have stayed. Fancy it here—for a governess! And afterwards I imagined—and I still imagine. And what I imagine is dreadful!"
"Not so dreadful as what *I* do," I replied.

So what, when "pushed to the wall," did Mrs. Grose imagine? That Miss Jessel had to leave Bly because her figure was in such a scandalous shape? And that afterwards she died in giving birth to a deceased base menial's bastard?

The relentless governess never lets up but "presses" Mrs. Grose for particulars (and adverse critical judgment) about Miles's reprehensible practice of going off with "the fellow" and spending hours with him. When the housekeeper, "visibly flushing," flounders in answer to the question whether Miles ever mentioned Miss Jessel's connection with Quint, the governess, hot on the trail, says, "Lord, how I pressed her now!" Then she shows herself doing so and Mrs. Grose suffering under the pressure:

"So that you could see he knew what was between the two wretches?"
"I don't know—I don't know!" the poor woman groaned.
"You do know, you dear thing," I replied; "only you haven't my dreadful boldness of mind, and you keep back, out of timidity and modesty and delicacy... But I shall get it out of you yet! There was something in the boy that suggested to you," I continued, "that he covered and concealed their relation."
"Oh, he couldn't prevent—"
"Your learning the truth? I dare say! But heavens" I fell with vehemence a-thinking, "what it shows that they must, to that extent, have succeeded in making of him!"

It struck me as curious—and rather like the illusion created by two mirrors reflecting a figure endlessly until it fades in the dim distance of greenish-gray glass—that even if the apparitions of Peter Quint and Miss Jessel are "identifiable" as former servants at Bly, they are also ghosts from James's own old story, and that these, even when he wrote it (a few years after the Civil War) were already ghosts from an older day—a period between the two great wars intended to insure for the common man the natural rights of life, liberty, equality, fraternity, and the pursuit of happiness. They carry on, in their silent ghostly way, the age-old battle cry of freedom for the underdog — especially freedom to love and marry across arbitrary social barriers.

Coquelin is an effective mouthpiece. When the three of them visit the old castle at Fossy that lifts "its dark and crumbling towers with a decided air of feudal arrogance from the summit of a gentle eminence," it is Coquelin who says they are at a "decidedly melancholy spot . . . haunted with the ghosts of the past. It smells of tragedies, sorrows, and cruelties . . . it's like the history of that abominable past of which it's a relic." Mademoiselle thinks she would have liked to live then, but not Coquelin: "Life is hard enough now . . . In those good old days . . . I should have been a brutal, senseless peasant, yoked down like an ox, with my forehead in the soil. Or else I should have been a trembling, groaning, fasting monk, moaning my soul away in the ecstacies of faith." That theme stays with him, turns up again at the end of his talk about the awful burden of despair that his ancestors suffered: "If we had lived five hundred years ago, in the shadow of these great towers . . . I suppose I should have gone into the Church. If I hadn't died from an overdose of inanition, very likely I might have lived to be a Cardinal." An intelligent man with his feet "stuck in the clay" had at least that way out: he could rise in the world — as a celibate within the Church; but never — except in a fairy-tale — could the son of a poor man marry a princess.

It struck me as curiously interesting that a fairy-tale never does end with the poor youngest of three sons becoming a cardinal or a pope, and a Cinderella an abbess or a prioress — living happily in their cells forever after. I shivered at the thought. Or because I was getting cold in that unheated so-called study.

The lamp chimney had become so black that the smoky flame gave little light. I had seen enough anyway; I had seen Coquelin climb "to the summit of the great tower" to enjoy the view "from the topmost platform." How remarkably he resembled the "unscrupulous traveller" of the governess's imagination, "curious," as she says, "in old houses" who "enjoyed the prospect from the best point of view" — a resemblance particularly noticeable when Coquelin takes off his hat to wave to Gabrielle and the boy, and, "finding it difficult to com-

with The Turn of the Screw

municate by sounds," tries to convey his meaning "by gestures of pretended rapture" over the immensity and beauty of the prospect. I had also heard him reproach Gabrielle, saying she couldn't quite reconcile it to her "dignity" to love a "nobody" — reminding me of the governess's saying to Mrs. Grose of the figure she saw on the tower: "He's like nobody . . . He has no hat." And I had observed that Coquelin left the Jesuits — he had studied with them three years — for no more explicit a reason than a "foolish breach of discipline" — a resemblance to Miles's never-explained dismissal from school. I closed the magazine, lit a candle, blew out the smoking lamp (which straightway belched out a nauseating stench), tucked the two *Atlantics* under my arm, and started back for the big chair in front of the fire.

Chapter IX

STARTING DOWN THE STAIRS,

I assured myself: this time I'm sure not to meet Peter Quint's ghost on the landing. What was I saying? Peter Quint's ghost? Or Peter Quince, ghost? Surely that rude mechanical, that hempen home-spun carpenter in *Midsummer-Night's Dream* wasn't going to do me out of my exciting discovery that James had peopled his little bogey tale with ghosts from a story of his own? No, certainly not. Peter Quince was also a "base menial"—just another reflection in the endless succession of ghosts in the mirror.

Even if that roomful of old books at Bly didn't contain Shakespeare (but of course it did) the governess had certainly seen Miles and Flora as competent little impersonators (capable, too, from the "mere exuberance of the gift," of the "most unimposed little miracles of memory") popping out at her in disguises as tigers, astronomers, and Shakespeareans. She and the children *lived* in a "cloud of music and love and success and private theatricals." Of course they had "done" *Midsummer-Night's Dream*—or parts of it. And I knew, oh, I knew, I knew, *what* parts! The very ones I had liked best when I was ten or so and they let me be the lion and roar as loud as ever I could, yet not so loud as to frighten the ladies.

It was her remembrance of Miles as an actor that prompted several vivid details of the mixed bait the governess holds out to Mrs. Grose—hoping to lure that stolid soul into a commitment that will then force her to believe the governess has not

A Stormy Night

"made it up" when describing Peter Quint. (As Myers tells it, proving that the ghost is real and not a mere hallucination depends upon a number of things: corroborative witnesses, revelation of otherwise unknown information, and the percipient's being able to give a description that others will recognize.) Why the governess describes the apparition as looking like an actor (although she has never seen one!) could come from her having seen Miles playing many parts—including that of a "rude mechanical" in *Midsummer-Night's Dream*.

Oh, I saw it all as I descended the stairs, saw it even after my candle went out, as of course it did when I missed a step, fell several more, and examined myself for broken bones as I rested for a few minutes on a landing. I saw and I heard—heard the voices of my companions in private theatricals when, in those earlier days, I roared the lion's part. I heard Peter Quince discovering a "marvelous convenient place for our rehearsal. This green plot shall be our stage, this hawthorn-brake our 'tiring house; and we will do it in action as we will do it before the Duke." Was it this "green plot" that James was trying to bring back from the past when he saw in Warwickshire a patch of smooth lawn set off by an encircling bend of the Avon? He did his best to believe it was a stage-set, even denying that the "voluminous sheep" across the river were mutton; he insisted they were there simply to make an appropriate backdrop for the comedy about to be put on.

I heard Puck telling that Titania, the fairy queen (shades of Janet and his curing of the love-lorn by substituting a man with red hair or a pig's head for the beloved image!), has as her attendant a "lovely boy, stol'n from an Indian king"—the very theme of fairies' stealing children I had wondered about before going upstairs. Weren't Miles and Flora from India? I couldn't remember, but I thought Douglas had said so.

And I heard the Duke's voice too, but as lisped out by a boy whose "miracle of memory" sometimes failed him because of his embarrassment:

> I never may believe
> Thethe antique fableth nor thethe fairy toyth.
> Loverth and madmen have thuch theething brainth,
> Thuch thayping fantathieth, that apprehend
> More than cool reathon ever comprehendth.

with The Turn of the Screw

It was astounding! I was lightheaded with it — or with the lateness of the hour and the lack of sleep. James, that old trickster, had shaped his fantasy, his fairy toy, in the same way — a fantasy that cool reason cannot comprehend. But — if taken as just another Midsummer-Night's dream, or nightmare! — the goings-on at Bly preserve the logic of dreams where almost anything is rather more than likely to happen. A "rosy sprite" like little Flora can turn into an ugly old woman; a charming man whom a lovesick girl expects to meet in her daydream can become a "nobody," a horror without a hat; an angelic boy who glitters like a fairy prince can be exposed as a monster of depravity who goes on long walks with a depraved tutor and is kicked out of school for saying "things." The lunatic, the lover, and the poet ("of imagination all compact") can be compressed into the person of a governess, a poor parson's daughter.

Sitting there in the dark on the landing of the stairs I really "saw" how the pieces fit together, how James had turned loose all of Oberon's fairy tribe to romp on the green grass at Bly. Oh, yes — I *saw! The Turn of the Screw* is indeed a fairy-tale — just as James says it is. The governess herself is "carried away," first by the master in Harley Street and then by the children, especially by Miles. "Of course," she says, "I was under the spell, and the wonderful part is that . . . I perfectly knew I was. But I gave myself up to it; it was an antidote to any pain."

I even caught Puck putting "love-juice" on her "sight" — and boggling the job. When she walks out during "her hour" in the long twilight thinking, "It would be as charming as a charming story suddenly to meet someone" who would stand there before her in the path and "smile and approve," what happens? Something goes wrong: Puck makes a mistake, or plays a prank. The Harley Street spell is broken and she sees a horror. She drags home wearily after her "collision" and her uncounted hours of wandering; "I must," she says, "have walked three miles." She makes a vague excuse to Mrs. Grose for her lateness and, "with the plea of the beauty of the night and of the heavy dew and wet feet," goes as soon as possible to her room. She is Hermia, after her search for Leander:

A Stormy Night

"Never so weary, never so in woe; Bedabbled with the dew and torn with briers." Or she is Thisbe, as Jessica (in her duet with Lorenzo about what happens in such a moonlit night) describes her:

> In such a night
> Did Thisbe fearfully o'ertrip the dew,
> And saw the lion's shadow ere himself
> And ran dismay'd away.

The governess who hoped to meet her Lysander or her Pyramus meets instead a shadow, a nobody, a horror.

And the children play pranks in the mischievous fairy tradition. Both of them blow out her candle to tease or bewilder her. Miles scares her with a "loud, high shriek . . . either of jubilation or terror" in accompaniment to a room-shaking thunder-clap. He tricks her with a musical charm into giving Flora a chance for a romp by herself. Although the governess compares his playing to David's playing for the mad Saul, his schemed-up little concert is like the magical fairy music in *Midsummer-Night's Dream:*

> *Oberon.* Silence awhile. — Robin, take off his head. — Titania, music call: and strike more dead than common sleep, of all these five the sense.
> *Titania.* Music, ho! music, such as charmeth sleep!

(The fairy king and queen knew, long before the hypnotists expressed their theories, that music was *one* of the methods.)

> *Puck.* Now, when thou wakest, with thine own fool's eyes peep.
> *Oberon.* Sound, music! (*Still music.*) — Come, my Queen, take hands with me, and rock the ground whereon these sleepers be.

The governess is just as "charmed" as the lovers in the play. She admits the "influence" (whether of fairy or hypnotist); and when she wakes from her strange sleep (of course she protests she was awake — as all the viewers of ghosts in the *Proceedings* protest), it is with her "fool's eyes" that she sees the apparition as big as a blazing fire out by the lake with Flora. Just how Puckish Miles is, I had missed before I was clued in by recognizing Peter Quint as Peter Quince. I read it all over carefully:

> He sat down at the old piano and played as he had never played, and if there are those who think he had better have been kicking a football I can only say that I wholly agree with them. For at the end of a time that under his influence I had quite ceased to measure I started up with a strange sense of having literally slept

with The Turn of the Screw

at my post. It was after luncheon, and by the schoolroom fire, and yet I hadn't really, in the least slept: I had only done something much worse—I had forgotten. Where, all this time, was Flora?

When the governess asks Miles where she is, his answer has all the joyous exuberance of one of Oberon's tribe:

"Why, my dear, how do I know?"—breaking moreover into a happy laugh which, immediately after, as if it were a vocal accompaniment, he prolonged into incoherent extravagant song.

Although the governess is teased, loved, led astray, and bewildered by the fairy-like spells, it is her own "fool's eyes" that make her see evil. And yet she almost knows what is really going on. She recognizes Miles' glittering fairy-prince quality when she cross-questions him after his exploit of being "bad" —going out on the lawn at midnight:

He was gentleness itself, and while I wagged my head at him he stood there more than ever a little fairy prince. It was his brightness indeed that gave me a respite....
"Then you didn't undress at all?"
He fairly glittered in the gloom. "Not at all. I sat up and read."

Oh, I was pleased to find how many things in James's *jeu d'esprit* could be explained in terms of *Midsummer-Night's Dream*. And pleased too in realizing that, if *The Turn of the Screw* is also just a dream (or a nightmare) I needn't "go about to expound" those parts of it that didn't come clear. For, as Bottom the Weaver says (on waking after Puck has removed the ass's head and the spell): "Man is but an ass, if he go about to expound this dream.... man is but a patch'd fool, if he will offer to say what methought I had." I had already been such an ass, but I didn't care. I was glad not to have to go on puzzling about ambiguities and inconsistencies that in a dream world would make good enough sense. What does it matter if Mrs. Grose says Flora wouldn't remember Peter Quint? Or that the governess says, in the midst of her account of her collision with that "nobody" that it seemed she had known him always? And then to contradict it later to Mrs. Grose? Or if it is Mrs. Grose who comes up with the suggestive name of Peter Quint? I wasn't going to care about all that, nor about the governess's inordinate knack for adding two and two and coming up with nine or seventeen. Why should I worry about the extravagant stretch she allows her imagination, her reckless disregard for

A Stormy Night

logical probabilities, and whether she's a victim of self-hypnosis or of a Svengali?

Several times she seems almost to realize that she is twisting the "facts" ridiculously to fit a predetermined pattern of evil. Normally—but nothing is normal in a dream—if she had her wits about her she would pay more attention to her occasional doubts and not push on to a catastrophe. Her doubts are enough to stop anyone thoroughly awake—or in his right mind. For instance, when she considers using Miles's room for a lookout post for observing what holds Flora spellbound at the window, she thinks "he might be innocent," that the risk is hideous, and so turns away. In the last chapter she is "paralysed," but only for a moment, by doubt:

> Those he liked? I seemed to float not into clearness but into a darker obscure, and within a minute there had come to me out of my very pity the appalling alarm of his being perhaps innocent. It was for the instant confounding and bottomless, for if he *were* innocent, what then on earth was *I*? Paralysed, while it lasted, by the mere brush of the question, I let him go a little, so that, with a deep-drawn sigh, he turned away from me again.

It was all the "stuff that dreams are made on"—not the craziness of a Cherubina or a Catherine: no Gothic heroine would have bothered to doubt her convictions. But I caught myself up—I was going on being an ass, trying to "expound." The death of Miles that had seemed earlier so incongruent needed no explication: it was like the death of Pyramus; with no place in reality—as Bottom makes clear: " . . . and let the prologue seem to say, we will do no harm with our swords, and that Pyramus is not kill'd indeed; and, for the more better assurance, tell them that I Pyramus am not Pyramus, but Bottom the Weaver: this will put them out of fear."

I tried to remember if James gives any similar reassurance in his "prologue"; I looked back, but couldn't make it out. Certainly in the end James gives no reassurance even resembling what Shakespeare does when Pyramus stabs himself and proclaims his "death":

> Now am I dead, now am I fled;
>   My soul is in the sky:
> Tongue, lose they light! Moon, take thy flight!
>   Now die, die, die, die, die.

with The Turn of the Screw

No sooner has Lysander announced the death than Theseus gives it the lie: "With the help of a surgeon he might yet recover, and prove an ass." Miles might yet recover and prove — what? I had resolved not to prove myself an ass by trying to expound a nightmare.

I got up then from my squatting position on the landing, retrieved the one *Atlantic* I could spot by the uncertain flame of my last match, and went on till I came to the place at the head of the first flight of stairs where I supposed the governess had stood when she "saw" there was "someone" on the landing below. I tried to see a "glimmer in the high glass and another on the polish of the oak stair." But I saw nothing. After all, I thought, I'm not a somnambulist in a Midsummer-Night's dream, but a serious, sane, sober scholar in the dead-of-a-winter-night's long darkness. I didn't know what time it was. It could be nearly morning. If dawn *were* breaking I couldn't see it because my eyes were dazzled by the flare of the match. Perhaps if I waited a second or two — I sat down on the top step and stared as hard as I could straight in front of me. Presently I did see a strange shapeless glow far down. Miss Jessel in her grief and woe — but a little faded? No, just a glow, as though a doubly or triply reflected light came from the lamp I had left burning by my chair. Perhaps I hadn't shut the door all the way. But the glow seemed to fade away while I watched.

I got to my feet and went on down as far as the landing where Peter Quint had stood — if he ever had been there at all. I felt a little queer, imagining that I was he — or Pierre, or Peter Quince (the name didn't matter any more) — come back from the dead looking for someone he loved — someone he must entice and lure into his own world of shadows. Turning to look up, I tried to pick out in the darkness the spot where the governess's white face would be staring down at me.

I shuddered. And, brushing my hand across my eyes, I felt my forehead dripping with icy sweat. There her ghastly face *was* — dim, almost invisible, but there, there! and dreadful in its fixity — no motion, no life! I knew that now there must be a glimmer in the high glass, but I dared not move my eyes to look. In another instant I recovered — just as I do when I realize that a snake in the path is really a crooked stick. I climbed

A Stormy Night

back up on all fours until my hand touched the solid reality of the *Atlantic* lying askew on a step near the top.

"Deceiving governess," I said, "and you too, Peter Quint or Quince, you're an airy nothing that the poet's eye or the lunatic's or the lover's gives a local habitation and a name!" Then, feeling the momentum of memorization, I finished the speech, lisping it out as I had heard it done in the old days when I roared the lion's part:

> Thuch trickth hath thtrong imaginathion,
> That, if it would but apprehend thome joy,
> It comprehendth thome bringer of that joy;
> Or in the night, imagining thome fear,
> How eathy ith a buthh thuppothed a bear!

And just as easily I went on supposing myself to be Peter Quint (or Quince) come back from the dead. And the sense of the governess's presence stayed with me: beaten and baffled I bent over, I hurried, I almost stumbled as I felt her awful eyes fixed on my "villainous back that no hunch could have more disfigured." Her inspiration, I supposed, for that touch came from seeing Miles, that accomplished Shakespearean actor, coming out from a confabulation in a corner as the villainous Richard III, he who made too free with everyone, who had his way with them all, even with the mourning wife of a recent victim of whose murder he openly boasted.

With my hand touching the newel post I knew I was at the bottom. I sank down to one of the lower steps and became Miss Jessel—my body half-bowed and my head, in an attitude of woe, in my hands. Who was I? If Quint was Pierre Coquelin and Peter Quince, who, then, was Miss Jessel? The governess up there staring down at me might know, and without seeing, "exactly what dreadful face" I had to show. But I didn't know. I might be Richard's mourning-widow bride or some other tragic heroine—most probably Lady Macbeth, for Miss Jessel was a lady—no fit mate for that base-menial Peter Quint, or that hempen-homespun, rude-mechanical, Peter Quince.

Chapter X

I CROSSED THE HALL,

stubbing my toes almost deliberately as I called myself an ass again for trying to expound characters not meant to be expounded. Who could possibly expound characters composed of bits of this and bits of that—not of old bones and mouldering cerements dug up in churchyards as Frankenstein's monster was, but of gathered themes, gestures, names, character traits, words said, situations, or parts of them, found in old novels or plays or scientific arguments about the human personality's survival of bodily death, hypnosis, lucid somnambulism, and the various *états mentaux*?

> [Mary Wollstonecraft Shelley's *Frankenstein or The Modern Prometheus* has been made available in paperback by Collier Books, New York.]

As I opened the door from the hallway (I *had* left it closed), shutting my eyes against the rush of heat and light, I suddenly realized—with all the clarity of an extra-lucid somnambulist—that all my theories were valid, all were contributing parts of an intended overall design. I couldn't think it all out logically right then, but I knew that Peter Quint was not really a base menial; he was a craftsman, a builder, a maker of some kind. And Peter Quince was the creative genius among those described by Theseus's Master of the Revels:

> Hard-handed men, that work in Athens here,
> Which never labour'd in their minds till now;
> And now have toil'd their unbreathed memories
> With this same play against your nuptial.

A Stormy Night

Peter Quince, hard-handed as he is, is called upon to write the prologue and to make a ballad of Bottom's dream—dream that a man were an ass to expound. And Pierre Coquelin was no ordinary base-menial either. His father had risen to the position of village tailor, and Coquelin went beyond that—thanks perhaps to his three years with the Jesuits—and made his living (after marrying his "lady") by painting portraits and doing "literary work." In the end, "in spite of his base birth, Coquelin acted with . . . superior temperance": he was no *sans-culotte*, but went to the scaffold with the Girondists.

The ghost who "lives" again in *The Turn of the Screw* is of the same clever breed—able to rise above his menial station. It is the governess who says: "You reminded him that Quint was only a base menial?" Mrs. Grose merely accepts the term— says grudgingly: "As you might say." She admits that she had too much respect for Quint to complain about him to the master. She was afraid too, afraid "of things that man could do. Quint was so clever—he was so deep." The master had let him have everything to say—even about the children; Quint was in charge at Bly. That much at least came clear to me. In compounding the complex character of Peter Quint, James gave him the qualities of a man rising from the dregs of society, not by becoming a "fasting monk, moaning" his "soul away in the ecstacies of faith," but by being clever—able to do something besides hard-handed work, able to "labour in his mind." Miles certainly admired and respected the man, as did the master—and Miles was never a fool, not even as shown through the eyes of the governess (except in dying for no reason at all at the end). It is the governess, with the pressured assistance of Mrs. Grose, who reduces an honorable, respectable, clever ghost to the semblance of a Frankensteinian monster who violates women and strangles children. Right then, sitting before the fire, I didn't like the governess at all. Even if she dreamed him up—as Mrs. Shelley did her monster, I couldn't forgive her. People shouldn't change good ghosts into bad ones—not even in dreams.

I was chilled from the stay in my so-called study and my adventures on the stairs. The oven-like heat of the enormous bed of coals seemed like the embrace of a living creature who

with The Turn of the Screw

brought back life to a man who had stayed for months in a dungeon. The cat, I noticed, had gone to the far side of the room to continue his everlasting nap on a chair. Presently I pushed my own chair back a little, but I gloated over the fire — a great incandescent mass aquiver with almost indiscernible points of blue flame. I was a privileged person, able to come out of icy studies and cold flights of stairs into a warm room with a fire that the devil in hell might have envied. I even shed a crocodile tear over the sad experiences of Mrs. Radcliffe's Schedoni and Maturin's villainous hypnotist suffering, albeit deservedly, in the horrible prisons of the Inquisition.

> [See Ann Radcliffe, *The Italian* (1797) and Charles Robert Maturin, *The Fatal Revenge or The Family of Montorio* (1807).]

It amused me that someone had said, probably Mrs. Barbauld, of *The Italian*, that if Mrs. Radcliffe was going to "improve" on her horrors she'd have to descend from the courts and prisons of the Inquisition to the infernal regions — to hell itself.

Actually shivering in the process of getting warmed up, I tried to collect my wits. There was something I wanted to look up or check, and it wasn't Gothic either. Oh yes, the strange unexplained death of Miles and whether James somehow manages to suggest that, like Pyramus, all he needed was a good doctor to make him recover. Perhaps there was a word or two on the order of Mrs. Grose's assurance to Flora at the lake: "It's all a mere mistake and a worry and a joke — and we'll go home as fast as we can."

Holding the book high to protect my face from the glowing heat I read the last paragraph:

> But he had already jerked straight round, stared, glared again, and seen but the quiet day. With the stroke of the loss I was so proud of he uttered the cry of a creature hurled over an abyss, and the grasp with which I caught him might have been that of catching him in his fall. I caught him, yes, I held him — it may be imagined with what a passion; but at the end of a minute I began to feel what it truly was that I held. We were alone with the quiet day, and his little heart, dispossessed, had stopped.

There it was, plain as could be: "his little heart, dispossessed, had stopped." And no one else was there — no Theseus, no Mrs. Grose — to say it was all a joke. I wanted to quit trying to understand, to expound, to explain, but out of sheer weary stubborn-

A Stormy Night

ness I could not let go. I knew I was taking it too seriously, forgetting that the whole thing was a fiction made up by the governess of the preamble to amuse herself, thus "embroidering" the "dull prose" of her "office." But why, even in a story, kill him off? Simply to come to a conclusive end — like a scholarly article for the journals? I pushed back further from the fire, even turned my chair a little sideways, as I read over all of the last chapter.

It puzzled me. Perhaps there is enough violence there to kill a boy of ten. The governess actually seems to wrestle with him at the same time that she browbeats him unmercifully, prying into his little secret sins — did he steal? what were those things he said? — things too bad for the masters to write home. She justifies her manhandling, her "blind movement of getting hold of him, drawing him close," by saying she's "instinctively keeping him with his back to the window" where Peter Quint has come into view "like a sentinel before a prison."

The narrator-governess of the preamble, it seemed, was exercising with particular skill her deftness in presenting a double picture: 1) the probable truth of a nasty situation, and 2) the frantic, hypnotized, crazy — I couldn't tell *what* she was — governess's distortion of that truth. The real truth seemed to me then that Miles dies of rough handling; the distortion, that the governess "saves" him by making him confess his piffling sins and keeping him from seeing what isn't even there — the ghost of Peter Quint. In a moment she describes *him*, not as a sentinel before a prison, but as the "thing at the window" whose "slow wheel" was "rather the prowl of a baffled beast." But all through that last chapter it is she, not the "thing at the window," who behaves like a beast. Her elation, her moans of joy, her shouts — what are they but insane bestial laughter? Yet, if one ignores her "joy" and her frenzied leaps and bounds, she does seem to behave like the Irish mother who calls her remaining children to her and holds them close so the fairies can't steal them. But no, I said to myself; fairies steal the *whole* child, not just his soul.

In my confusion — for I mistrusted my own thinking (I *had* been up a long time), I poured myself a cup of coffee, but it was so rank and strong from sitting too long on the hearth that I

with The Turn of the Screw

spat out the first sip and dumped the rest back in the pot. In spite of her insistence that her roughness is motivated by "pure tenderness" and her sternness all for his "judge, his executioner" (who are these, I asked myself—this judge, this executioner?), what her behavior adds up to is pure torture—physical and mental. I had to give up on my old opinion that his death is a Pyramus joke—a healthy boy seeming to die of fright. No. She kills him as a child might kill a kitten—carrying it around by the neck; as a big old dog might "worry" a puppy to death—playing with it; or as a Frankensteinian monster might strangle a child in resentment and rage—or just for kicks.

Certainly the effect on Miles is far worse than could be expected from a forced confession of his little sins. After the first round she says: "I held him to my breast, where I could feel in the sudden fever of his little body the tremendous pulse of his little heart." When she says she shook him (for pure "tenderness"), she adds the result: "He looked in vague pain all round the top of the room and drew his breath, two or three times over, as if with difficulty." When she "let [s] him go a little" (Peter Quint not right then at the window to justify her clutch), Miles is soon "at some distance, . . . still breathing hard and again with the air, though now without anger for it, of being confined against his will." When her sternness makes him "avert himself again," she behaves like a cat playing with a mouse; his *movement,* she says, makes *her,* "with a single bound and an irrepressible cry spring straight upon him." Then, apparently to disguise her beastly behavior, she gives another reason for the "wildness" of her "veritable leap": "there again, against the glass, as if to blight his confession and stay his answer, was the hideous author of our woe." It is always she, not the "baffled beast" standing sentinel outside, who grasps him, holds him tight, springs, leaps, and bounds.

Whether she has Miles, at one time or another, by the shoulders, the waist, the head, the neck—to keep him from seeing the alleged "face of damnation"—is never clear. But it is clear that he has difficulty breathing and that his face is contorted. When she announces that the "coward horror" is there for the last time, Miles gives his head a "frantic little shake for *air and light*"; a little later his face gives "again, round the room,

A Stormy Night

its *convulsed* supplication" [*our author, not Henry James, is responsible for the italics*].

Yes, I had to face it: the "joke" was on me for not realizing earlier that Miles is no Pyramus; he is simply "worried" to death by a governess gone berserk, or—?

I turned back to the book to see if I could find any "preparation" for such a violent death. Of course it's everywhere in a sense—in all the hints at her obsession, her lucidity, her strange hushes, her seeing ghosts, and so on, but I thought I might find some earlier hint that she had a tendency toward violence. In Chapter 22, after Mrs. Grose and Flora have gone, the governess becomes "very grand, very dry," and "quite remarkably firm"—putting on a nonchalant air for the benefit of the servants, to defy their confused and questioning stare. She decrees that meals for her and Miles shall be served "in the ponderous pomp of the room outside the window of which" she had seen Peter Quint—this, to "mark for the house the high state" she "cultivated." Waiting there in that ponderous pomp she seems—with part of her mind (for in many ways she is a house divided against itself, like the hysterical cases of Azam, Janet, and many others)—to be premeditating some action—but what it is she never makes clear. She decides that with her "rigid will" she must shut her eyes "as tight as possible to the truth" that what she has to deal with is "revoltingly against nature." She decides to push on to her "monstrous ordeal," in a "direction unusual" and "unpleasant," "but demanding, after all, for a fair front, only another turn of the screw of ordinary human virtue." Does she merely intend to extort, by whatever means necessary, a "confession" from Miles that will justify her? How far is she willing to go in her "monstrous ordeal... revoltingly against nature"? I realized she is using the expression "turn of the screw" in a different way than Douglas, or someone, used it in the preamble. But that was no help; I still didn't know what it was she planned to do that was unusual, unpleasant, revoltingly against nature. It *seemed* that she meant to get rid of the boy so he couldn't tattle on her to his uncle in Harley Street. And then to make up a story about it that would satisfy the better side of her nature.

Chapter XI

I WAS ABOUT TO SEE

what I could find in the next chapter when the big lamp began to act up—the flame galloping around the circular wick in dizzying fluctuations. It was almost out of oil. I jumped up, thinking I'd blow it out to avoid being in disgrace for letting the wick burn, but everything went black for a moment—I was weak from lack of sleep and the stuffiness of the warm room. I sank down in my chair again and decided to let nature take its course with the lamp. The book had fallen to the floor. I let it lie. No more reading for that night; I was certainly not going to prowl around with a candle hunting for the oil can.

Idly I watched the fire—growing dim in its ruddy glare when the lamp flared high, but brightening again when the lamp went almost out. I was amused that one can see more light in the dark than in the light. Crazy paradox, but probably true! I'd be better able to think out all my ideas in the dark—able to think how I would write a coherent, sensible, definitive article for Baldy Twitchell. I knew I ought to go to bed, but I had promised myself to make a night of it. I couldn't give up before "the dusk of earliest morning"—to borrow a phrase from the governess. I turned my head to stare at the windows—not a glimmer anywhere, not even in the east windows at the far end of the long room.

Even when the lamp had finished its agonized expiring, the ruddy glow of the fire went through changes, but most of them in the direction of smothering itself with ashes. Dimmer and dimmer the glow became until—well, at any moment I might

A Stormy Night

expect the red-eyed monkey of Dr. Hesselius's bachelor-vicar Mr. Jennings to vanish and leave me with nothing but a cold bare hearth. My common sense told me I should either build up the fire before the room got cold, or cover it with ashes so the fire would keep and go to bed. But it might be morning any minute and I was too comfortable to move.

To pass the time and to keep from dropping off [*to sleep?*] I started thinking over what I might write for Baldy. I could begin, for instance:

> In spite of being a horror story pure and simple, and one with the most dreadful horrible end—the bestial barehanded murder of an innocent child—*The Turn of the Screw* is a magnificent exhibition of Henry James's technical skill as a story-teller. He acts on his own precept that "the flower of art blooms only where the soil is deep"; "it takes a great deal of history to produce a little literature" [see James's *Hawthorne* (New York, 1880), p. 3; and pp. 42, 63-64]. "History" for James means the story of the past, not as recorded in history books but as interpreted by novelists, dramatists, and poets—those who intuitively understand that clumsy life presents the wrong truths that the artist must replace with the right truth. In accordance then with his own theories, James evokes ghosts from the past—from Gothic novels, including the satires on them, from his own earlier "Gabrielle de Bergerac," from *Midsummer-Night's Dream* (classic fore-runner of the "pyschologists")—with its fairies, its rude mechanicals, and its sage philosophy on the powers of the imagination. The governess of the tale is a synthetic character representing Imagination: she is lunatic, lover, and poet, "of imagination all compact."

But is she? Baldy would expect me to be dogmatic, with no wishy-washy conjecturing. Could I so flatfootedly say she *represents* Imagination? Hardly! She is too real, too damned real! At least, thinking of her as symbolic made me more sympathetic about the dreadful murder at the end. But what I had started to think up wasn't true—it didn't cover enough ground. So I started over:

> In spite of being a fairy tale pure and simple, dreamed-up by a charming governess-novelist who is horrified at the possibility of what might happen if she let her imagination run riot under the influence of a roomful of old books, *The Turn of the Screw* is a horror story of nightmare extravagance terminating with the pretended murder of an innocent boy by—of all people—his governess who, her wits addled by reading about rapacious, incestuous, murdering monks and monsters, acts out, perhaps under

with The Turn of the Screw

hypnotic suggestion whether self-induced or otherwise, the part of such a creature torturing a child she has been led to believe is a devil incarnate, or she is "saving" him from such a devil, or whatever else needs to be included at this point—but that the tale is all the product of imagination, so the murder is not real. And neither, I might add, are the ghosts, the governess, or the children, because the first governess merely makes them all up. Some bits of fact, perhaps—

I was obviously not getting anywhere in my efforts to think out a logical and clear-cut paper for Baldy. I couldn't take hold in the right place. How could I work around to the social comment: that even ghosts are the victims of malicious gossip, that a governess may go crazy as much from her ambiguous social status as from reading fiction, that James, old die-hard that he is, reworks, but in reverse, the favorite old fairy-tale theme of youngest son of poor woodchopper finally winning the hand of the king's daughter, Cinderella finally getting her prince charming, and James's own tales of *boobus Americanus* of either sex finally getting or not getting the Italian prince or princess—and tying the theme in with popularized case histories of women with hysterical fixations on absurdly idealized members of the opposite sex? The poor governess is defeated before she starts—how can she, a poor parson's daughter, win, with propriety, the love of either the master or the children? Of course she has to change the too romantic image of the master, either with or without a hypnotist's suggestion, into a monster of iniquity so she can forget him, and the children— she has to decide that Flora behaves like a street child and that Miles—well, the best I could figure it out (but I wasn't *sure*): she kills him in a rage of defeat, or her Svengali, whoever *he* might be, persuades her to get rid of him.

My ideas were too scattered. I couldn't find the right thread to string them on. The social comment wasn't intrinsically important to James. At least, not so much so as I was making out. What mattered to him was how a clever alert human mind works in trying to cope with an impossible—or at least a difficult—problem. And yet I could see *The Turn of the Screw* as an allegory, with the children and the master representing the aristocracy, the housekeeper the masses, and the governess the jealous clergy—rabidly eager for more power and more social recognition.

A Stormy Night

Random thoughts and questions kept popping into my mind. What about the satire on the psychologists—on cures of lovesick females, the pressuring of Freud, and the "fishing" that Lodge objected to in Dr. Phinuit's faked attempts at omniscience? Oh, yes, it was there; and it was funny: in spite of her pressuring and her fishing, the governess never does get all her "proof" nor an answer to her most important question: "What were those things?" I snickered a little, imagining her, with her insatiable curiosity—so like an expert at psychological analysis—torturing the "victim" of her "lucidity" to death before she gets what she's after! Why, all she proves is that little boys are mortal!

A couple of times I caught myself in the midst of falling asleep. I actually heard myself start to snore. I straightened up from my slouch in the chair and watched the fire to keep my eyes open—counting how often I could catch a fragment of live coal in the act of diminishing itself and falling lower and lower in the fire. I thought for a scary moment that the red-eyed monkey was there, trying to dig into the coals and then pull them in after him. But no. There was nothing there but glowing coals.

Chapter XII

SUDDENLY

I was startled by the sound of footsteps behind me. The cat again? No. The tread was too heavy, too measured and majestic. Someone "curious in old houses," someone without a hat? A burglar, curious also about what valuables the old house might contain? Believing that the easiest way in the world to get shot is by apprehending a burglar, I didn't move a muscle. I'd let him take whatever he called valuables and get away scot free.

But the footsteps continued their measured pace, to and fro, right in the room, not moving on to the dining room in search of silver and plate, but staying there behind me, going back and forth, back and forth, like an animal in a cage. I didn't dare look behind me because my head would show in silhouette against the coals, but I turned my eyes so far on either side—*trying* to look behind me—that the andirons swapped places before the glare of the fire. Then I saw as in a mirror the room behind me and a figure walking there with ponderous pomp, very grand and dry. While I watched, it stopped in front of the tall mirror between two bookcases, adjusted its long gorgeous robe—much too big for it—by pulling it up through a belt or rope around the middle. From this ceinture hung a weight of heavy keys. The figure pushed its head-gear—whether a crown, a bishop's miter, or a saucepan, I wasn't sure—around at different angles, concluding with the tailpiece in the rear.

Then I realized, as the intruder reached up for a book on a high shelf, that the real face was hidden by a serenely imper-

A Stormy Night

turbable mask. He — or so I thought: I soon corrected myself: *she* opened the book and began to read, making sweeping dramatic gestures all the while. I caught some words, but they didn't make very good sense.

"Out, out, damned candle! Life is but a dream!" and "Then you *do* know; you *are* guilty! Confess this instant! Toil and trouble, boil and bubble. Life is but a bubble or bauble or babble. Life is but a dream — signifying nothing. He's a nothing, a nobody — with red hair and without a hat." After more prancing around, all before the tall mirror to catch the effect, she went on: "If it were done, then 'twere well 'twere done quickly! But smile, smile, smile — and be a villain, be a villain!" It was the governess play-acting when she "dipped" into her room; or it was Breuer's Fraulein in her "private theatre." I felt lucky to have such an inside track on what was really going on — the governess rehearsing and not knowing I was there!

Fascinated by the spectacle, I had forgotten to be careful and before I knew it I felt myself clutched by strong arms and dragged bumpingly from my chair, down the corridor, around a corner, downstairs, upstairs, bangedly-bump, downstairs again, and pushed, shoved, pulled — even through places so narrow I thought they'd never get me through — to arrive at last at an underground cavern that I hadn't known belonged to the place. There I was strapped to a table, stretched, unstretched, tossed to the floor, stamped on, and weighted down with old cellar doors, mill stones, and all kinds of heavy rubbish that accumulates in cellars and dungeons. I tried to call for help, but I managed only a crazy rattling in my nose. A light, getting stronger and stronger, glared in my eyes. And then there *she* was — beady eyes glittering through slits in her placid mask. She shouted at me:

"Then you do know what she died of? Admit it, confess, tell, before I have to press you further. Confess! What did she die of? You poisoned her?" I couldn't say a word. "Then you *are* guilty?"

She turned to the others and ordered more pressure: "Bring the barn door, the anvil; bring the old pony! I'll get it out of her yet!"

"Her?" I asked myself in horror. Had they somehow changed

my sex? Then I realized it was all a mistake; she had taken me for Mrs. Grose. I tried to explain: "You have the wrong person. I'm not who you think I am," but as before I could make no articulate sound. I couldn't speak. I couldn't move. And then I felt a weight as of the whole world rolled on top of what was already too much. My flesh and even my bones were flattening to the hard stone pavement.

Impenetrable darkness followed but it didn't last; again the glaring light in my eyes, and she was still there — very much there — screaming for the pilniwinkis, the thumbikins [*Scottish and English terms for "thumbscrew"*].

"We'll put the screws on him, get him in the pinch, make him tell what he said!" I was glad to hear the "him": at least I wasn't Mrs. Grose any more. I tried to sit on my hands but it was no use. In a moment the screws were on, but not tight enough to hurt. "Now then," she said, "screw your courage to the sticking point and tell me everything."

I felt my mouth open to speak, but nothing came out.

"Aha!" she said. "He's there, the coward horror, there — to spoil your confession and stay your answer! I'll fix him! And then, my dear" — she patted my hand — "I'll take care of you." She got up, bundled up her long robe, and scrambled around, picking up potatoes, turnips, anything she could find, and then pitched — rapid-fire. Squash, bang! I heard things hit somewhere and even saw the ink bottle smash and the ink spread, run, thick like blood, down the wall. She was back with me in a jiffy.

"First, my dear," said she, holding my hand, "we'll try reason and persuasion. I want to save you, *save* you from your wrong-headed folly. Simply confess, tell me what you said, and then your precious soul will be saved! Come now, spit it out. What were those things you said — spreading evil within the flock?"

I tried to speak but it was no use. I might have been in a dream for all the good it did me.

"This hurts me more than it does you," she said, pitching her voice a shade higher and giving a turn to the screw. "You realize, I'm sure, that heresy is a sin, not only against your own soul but against God, against the Holy Office, against

A Stormy Night

Church and State. What were these blasphemous things you said?"

I would have spoken if I could to ask her what I was accused of, what blasphemy I was supposedly guilty of. But her answers to my unasked questions came in a torrent:

"If you were not a malefactor you would not now be in my power [see *John 18:30*]. You have set yourself up too high. Now then, what did you say? Was it about purgatory — that you don't believe in it? Come! Answer!" She turned the screw again but I scarcely felt the pinch. "Confess and be saved," she went on. "Be stubborn and be damned! Perhaps you deprecated the monastic state. Did you? Answer me this instant!" She gave another turn to the screw and that turn hurt. "Remember you are sinning against God, the Holy Office, the Church, the State, your own precious soul, and against *me*!"

To emphasize the "me" she gave the screw such a nasty twist that tears came to my eyes. If my answer had not been stayed, if I could have spoken, I'd have tried to reason with her, tell her she was a ghost from too far in the past — the Spanish Inquisition — so long gone. Then, as though she had read my mind, she pushed ahead in time:

"You are guilty of heresies blasphemously expressed against the foundations of the Christian religion. You have said that prayers for the dead will bring about an earlier resurrection?" Was I to be banished, I wondered, as Caroli was from Lausanne? "And, worse," she panted, "you have denied the tripersonality of the Godhead and the eternity of the Son! You have! You have! You know you have!"

My God, I thought, even if Calvin should recommend a merciful beheading, she'll have me burned at the stake!

"Besides, you believe in polygamy and rebaptism at thirty!" She was prancing all over the place, gesticulating wildly. "Don't be another Charles the First," she howled. "Don't lose your head! *Confess* you don't believe in predestination, that the last shall be first, the first last, and in the utter depravity of man! Confess! Repent! Retract — and be saved!"

I must have moved my head in my effort to speak, for she furiously screeched: "You would, would you, shake your head at me! Think yourself wiser than your instructress, than your pre-

with The Turn of the Screw

ceptor! I'll shake your head for you!" Suiting the action to the word, she got me by the shoulders and shook me so hard that my poor aching head banged miserably on the hard stone floor. Next, she wrenched at my hand and, with all her strength, turned the screw for the last time — as far as her strong young hands could make it go. Her mask had fallen off and I saw her dreadful face — oh, horrible! Words fail me; I can't describe it.

I think I screamed, but it may have been she, for I heard — there at the last — her wild yell: "Oh, you *are* guilty! You are! You are! But I'll save you, I'll save you!"

In a single bound she was upon me, her knees on my chest and stomach and her hard hands tight around my throat, squeezing, squeezing, squeezing. I tried to break the straps that held down my arms and legs. It was no use. I felt my tongue coming out of my mouth, my eyes bulging in the brilliant light, my heart pounding violently and then — fluttering, fluttering to a stop.

All sensation left me except the cold, the terrible cold. I ached all over. But presently I realized that something was warm on my face. The morning's sun, not yet high, was shining in my eyes. My necktie and most of my torn-up collar lay on the floor not far away from me — nor from the cat who had found, of course, the warmest place in a room where the fire has gone out.

ABOUT THE AUTHOR

Muriel West was born in Pennsylvania, educated in Wisconsin (B.A.) and Arkansas (M.A. and PhD.), worked in New York City at a number of different writing jobs, and now teaches English at Southern Illinois University in Carbondale. She has published a number of poems and pieces of literary criticism in various journals. She is an authority on alchemy in literature. *A Stormy Night With The Turn Of The Screw* is a brilliant and refreshing example of literary criticism at its inventive and creative best.

3-30-66